FIELD SERVICE MANAGEMENT

Other books by Merlin Stone

Product Planning
Marketing and Economics
How to Market Computers and Office Systems

Field Service Management

MERLIN STONE AND ANTONY WILD
of Midas Consultants

Gower

Published by Gower Publishing Company Limited,
Gower House, Croft Road, Aldershot, Hants GU11 3HR, England

and

Gower Publishing Company,
Old Post Road, Brookfield, Vermont 05036, U.S.A.

British Library Cataloguing in Publication Data

Stone, Merlin
 Field service management

 1. Service industries - Management. I. Title
 338.4   HD9980.5

Library of Congress Cataloguing in Publication Data

Stone, Merlin
 Field service management

 1. Service industries - Management. I. Title.
 HD9980.5.S76 1985   658   84-27898

ISBN 0-566-02477-2

Copy generated on a Xerox 8000 Series Information Processor
Printed in Great Britain at the University Press, Cambridge

To our wives
Ofra (Stone) and Rosemary (Wild)

CONTENTS

PREFACE

Companies from a variety of industries provide service to customers through after-sales service to equipment. This book is aimed at companies which:
- Have a field service operation, whether for products supplied by themselves or others, whether in customer sites or in 'own use' sites, or
- Sell products which are serviced in the field by a third party, or
- Sell products maintained by 'send/bring in and repair/exchange' methods

These activities are common to most suppliers of electrical, electronic or mechanical hardware. This book is the result of our consulting, survey and training work with the service operations of a range of such companies, from computing and office automation companies, to vending machine suppliers.

Objectives of the book

This book does not describe in detail how to set up and run a service organisation. It provides a management overview, with the emphasis on different approaches rather than details. The objectives of the book are:

1. To enable managers and planners of the above types of operation to take a fresh look at the structure, policies, management performance and cost of their organisations, to find ways of improving the level of service delivered, reliability, cost, and so on.
2. To give managers responsible for service on new product ranges or in new companies some ideas on how to structure their service operation, to budget and plan for it.
3. To provide general management, business planners, and managers in marketing, R & D, production and other functional areas that affect or are affected by service performance, with an improved ability to take service factors into account in their decisions.

Structure of the book

In Chapter 1, we outline the total service system which encompasses product design, manufacture, marketing, machine service, spare parts inventory, refurbishing and customer service. A primary objective of this system is to deliver profit to the supplier and satisfaction to the customer. For this system to work, service and other management need a clear view of their main tasks, which are also outlined.

Chapters 2 and 3 cover the demand for service. In Chapter 2, the main determinants of demand are investigated. Chapter 3 explains the service market information system, including techniques for researching service demand.

Once the parameters of demand for equipment service and customer service have been specified, the service product can be specified. This applies both to service aspects which depend mainly on design and engineering factors (e.g. uptime) and to service products (contracts, prices, customer care). Chapters 4 and 5 concentrate on design and engineering factors. Chapter 4 analyses the relationship between service and design, manufacturing and marketing. Asset management and related life-cycle cost approaches are discussed, together with quality approaches to design and manufacture. Chapter 5 focuses on the role of marketing strategy in integrating design, manufacturing and service aspects, particularly for new products.

Chapters 6 and 7 cover the specification of service products. Chapter 6 sets out various approaches to achieving 'customer service orientation'. Chapter 7 investigates the detailed options for individual service products.

Chapters 8 to 13 cover service delivery systems. Without effective delivery systems, the best laid service plans can come unstuck. In Chapter 8, we consider operating methods. Chapter 9 covers a major element of service resourcing - spare parts inventory.

Given decisions on operating methods, an incentive, targetting and control mechanism must be created to ensure that decisions are implemented. This is the subject of Chapters 10 to 12. Chapter 10 covers targets and control systems, Chapter 11 covers financial planning and control, and Chapter 12 covers productivity, performance and planning. Chapter 13 considers different organisational options and approaches to manpower management. Finally, Chapter 14 provides an overview of ways of increasing service profit. The Appendix discusses the effect of third party service on the market.

Checklists
An important feature of this book is the provision of comprehensive checklists of questions at the end of each chapter. These may be used for occasional review of particular elements of the service operation, or for a comprehensive service audit.

Merlin Stone
Antony Wild

1 MANAGING A CHANGING SERVICE SYSTEM

Not so many years ago, the future of after-sales service seemed easy to predict. Most economies were growing steadily, producing an accelerating diffusion of electro-mechanical equipment of all kinds, in businesses and households. This increasing installed base of equipment seemed likely to produce an exploding demand for service engineers of all kinds. Many companies were uncertain as to whether they would be able to recruit enough manpower of the right calibre, particularly as traditional sources of trained manpower (the armed forces, public utilities) were releasing fewer staff of the right kind. Many larger companies embarked on substantial training programmes to ensure that their own supply of skilled manpower would be secure.

The electronic revolution

Then came the electronic revolution. Within a few years, the nature of the need for after-sales service had changed radically, but in a way which was difficult to foresee. Equipment reliability improved in leaps and bounds, while repair was aided by increased modularity in design and improved diagnostic equipment. By itself, this would have reduced the demand for skilled service staff. But the revolution also led to massive reductions in the price of many items of equipment, which in turn led to increased demand. In a number of areas (e.g. computing, telecommunications equipment), the installed base has exploded. Electronic technology has not stood still, so engineers are faced with much more rapid evolution in the technology of the equipment they service. However, they usually have to service quite advanced equipment in parallel with older equipment, incorporating out-of-date technologies. In many cases, the importance of software has created a demand for a new type of service operation, dedicated to tracking faults in software.

Customer service or machine service?

Another increasingly prominent factor is the growing need for customer service. The complexity of many types of equipment, an increasing tendency for customers to be dependent on it, and the increased diffusion of equipment among non-technical users, have all combined to create an environment in which the philosophy of customer service really pays. Many (though not all) customers are looking for much more than machine service after purchase. They may be looking for psychological values involved in reassurance, security and advice, as well as technical service, additional equipment and supplies. The use of the term 'customer service' is not dependent on some vague, idealistic, interpretation of the role of service. The term is used to signal the fact that it is the customer who pays, not the machine! Satisfying customer requirements in a way that contributes to the company's business objectives is therefore a central aim of the service operation.

Customer service can be a key competitive weapon for equipment suppliers, helping to capture and defend market share, as well as to contribute substantial profits. But a strong and effective customer service operation needs to be carefully planned and managed. The experience of many companies is that it is all too easy to lose customers and money by not treating customer service with the care that it requires.

CUSTOMER SERVICE - THE HYBRID DISCIPLINE
One reason why after-sales service is problematic for some companies is that it is a hybrid. Its objectives usually relate to equipment service. Yet it is also a service industry, providing a service to customers, and sharing many characteristics with other service industries, such as retailing, transport, and banking. Let us examine some of these factors.

Control over product
The supplier of service may think that he controls his product less than the manufacturing company, because the conditions under which the service is delivered and how it is used by the customer, are not easy to control. This difference can be exaggerated. One of the fundamental tenets of marketing is that it is not so much the product that counts, as the perception of the product. This is determined by the customer who, although heavily influenced by the manufacturer (via the technical specification of the product and via advertising), is also influenced by the channel through which he obtains the product, his own experience and background, and so on. However, it is probably fair to say that unless the service supplier makes a concerted effort to control the conditions under which the service product is delivered, there is more room for problems arising out of inappropriate customer perceptions. To some extent, this may relate to the next factor (dependence on people). For the

2

customer service operation, the implication is clear - the first step in making service policy is to understand the customer and why he needs service.

Dependence on people

Another factor shared by most service organisations is dependence on people. Although most service suppliers are trying to automate the service operation and reduce its labour content, in general service is people-intense. This, combined with the foregoing point, means that the image of the service product may be quite heavily influenced by the people who deliver it. However, the people who deliver the service are often recruited not for their ability to deliver service to customers, but for their command of the technical side of the job (e.g. machine service). Paradoxically, in organisations with a direct sales force selling equipment which has to be maintained, this force is the only group trained to handle customers, although they are usually in less frequent contact with customers than service engineers.

Need for customer orientation

The need for customer orientation is paramount in a service organisation, since the people, the production and the marketing are nearly identical. The service is created, sold and delivered by more or less the same people. This means that senior management has to have a very clear view as to how the customer-orientation of the service organisation is to be delivered. A retail organisation can no more rely on maintaining 100% stock levels as a service policy than a field service organisation can rely on a two hour response time.

A major element in achieving customer orientation is that the staff themselves must believe that they are a crucial part of the story, believing that their job is to solve customer problems and increase customer satisfaction, not just sell a service product or fix a machine. They must be trained to listen, to identify problems and communicate to customers and other staff. But this is unlikely to work well if the staff themselves are not listened to.

Management style

This creates the need for a certain style of management. Some hold that this style should be demonstrated by action, not words (i.e. listening to staff problems and acting on them). Superficial communications programmes will not achieve much. Some companies believe that the only way to achieve this is through extensive involvement of staff in decision making, even if only on a day-to-day level. This approach tends to generate an ability to handle problems independently, without recourse to authority (and consequent delay). The main risk here is of loss of control. It is easy for smaller organisations to follow this kind of principle. However, failure to improve in this area can lead to severe problems for large companies, with lack of motivation leading to poor customer service, inefficiency, high costs, lost business and eventually industrial relations problems caused by the consequent need to contract. In some cases, over-functionalisation (responsibility for tasks rather than for customers) is the source of problems. This applies particularly to offices handling requests for after-sales service. Teams of service engineers, sales and administrative staff, dedicated to defined groups of customers, have sometimes produced dramatic increases in customer loyalty, yielding increased sales and profitability. For these reasons, the creation of a marketing department in a service company should never be allowed to cause staff to think that the job of marketing is now 'taken care of'.

This approach must flow through into how staff are managed and assessed. They need to be assessed not just on technical criteria (e.g. fixing machines), but also on their ability to create and retain business from customers, while improving customer satisfaction. However, this can cause a problem. The skills required to solve customer problems may be non-routine, requiring creativity and initiative, while technical skills may be more routine.

The integrated approach
All the above factors imply that the approach to service must be integrated, with all the elements of service (contracts, prices, level of service, administrative systems, staff recruitment, deployment and training, the image projected by PR and advertising) co-ordinated to transmit the message of customer orientation and customer problem solving. Service organisations under profit pressure which react by reducing resource levels may pay a heavy price for failure to consider the impact of this change on the level of service, both directly and through reduced staff morale. This implies that policy responsibility must not be over-functionalised (e.g. split between sales, marketing, area management, after-sales service, and so on).

This is all very well in theory. However, the need to simplify in order to manage and to obtain economies of scale dictates that not every customer's need can be met easily. The market must be segmented according to different customers' needs for service. For example, airlines differentiate between business class and tourist class, railways between first and second class, banks between large and small accounts, and so on.

Service is a business

If we had to summarise these lessons from looking at service industries, it would be in the statement:

'Service is a business'.

This does not, of course, mean that customer service is a business independent of product sales. But it is a major component in business success. Therefore all the best business principles need to be applied to its management. This book aims to show how they can be applied. Given the limitations of space, we have focused in this book on those areas which we consider to be the most crucial for companies over the next few years.

MANAGING THE SERVICE SYSTEM

The purpose of this section is:

- To enumerate the components of the service system, and show how they are related to each other (i.e. to produce a system map).
- To give an overview of what is needed to manage the system.

The system map

The logical start point of a service system map is with the customer, not the machine or the engineer. The objective of most service functions is to provide some level of customer satisfaction for which charges can be made (either directly, in the form of service payments, or indirectly, in the form of a premium on equipment prices).

The customer has a demand for three kinds of service:

- Equipment services - the output of the equipment.
- After-sales technical service - the provision of support to resolve downtime, provide up-time, and so on.
- Customer service - the structuring and management of relationships between the customer and the supplier so as to ensure that the customer's

perception of the first two kinds of service is appropriately positive. This service is not something that the customer has to be forced to demand - most customers' need for this kind of service is "psychologically" more deeply embedded than that for the first two.

The customer might see the situation as shown in Figure 1.1

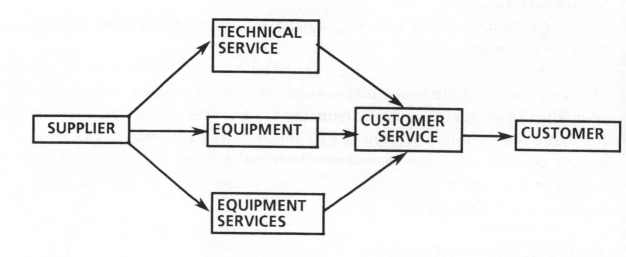

Figure 1.1 The flow of service

Suppliers may view this figure from the technical standpoint (the supplier supplies equipment and technical service to maintain that equipment, and the equipment then provides equipment services to the customer). Customers may see it very differently. Technical service, the equipment and its services may be viewed through a filter which is their perception of the level of customer service received. Customer service should perhaps be thought of as a major product of the service operation, and technical service as a major contributor to the delivery of that product.

The technical system, the one most familiar to field service managers, is itself a very complex system, as shown in Figure 1.2. The figure represents the major factors which affect the three kinds of service delivered to the customer. The formally defined service function (which in some companies may include the spare parts and the physical distribution activities) can be seen to be part of a wider system in which marketing, manufacturing and design play an equally

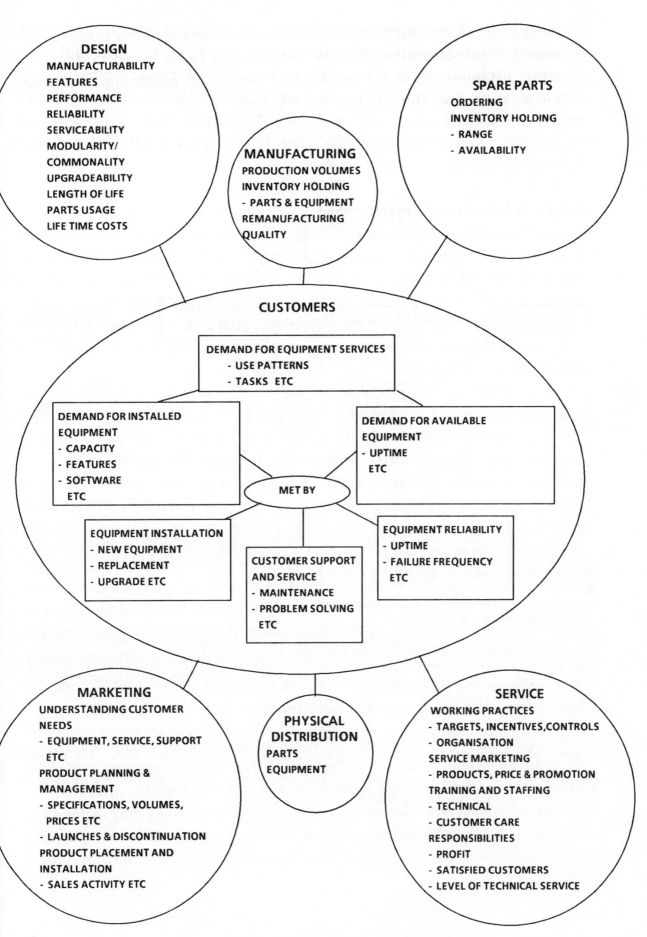

Figure 1.2 The Technical Service System

important part. Service operations often see themselves as operating within the constraints imposed by these other functions. As we shall see in this book, this is a narrow interpretation of the role of service, which at its best can play a major part in securing and retaining customers profitably. This is because service staff may be in very close contact with customers. They may provide much of the data on which the overall system is dependent. They may also be the most effective channel for delivering customer service.

OVERVIEW OF MANAGEMENT TASKS

Even when shown in this simple diagram, the picture looks very complex. Human factors can be seen to be very important, particularly in the areas of call handling, engineer staffing, and understanding the demand for customer service. Therefore, approaches to service management which rely solely upon highly optimised technical factors are not always appropriate. These approaches often assume perfection in planning, management and control systems (and often perfect customers!).

A central problem in field service management is making policy work. What works depends not only on the design of policy, but also on how management implements particular policies, from the organisation through which they do it, and the people within that organisation, to the systems for motivating and controlling them. The focus of this book is therefore as much on implementing service decisions as on service policy. However, on the assumption that a good policy well implemented is better than a bad policy well implemented, we start with a model service planning process.

Why a planning process?

In many companies, the service organisation has evolved as a technical adjunct to the marketing operation. Its main task was to ensure that physical reliability standards were maintained, and that no customers were so dissatisfied as to turn to competitors. As service takes a more central role in business, there is a need for a more self-conscious attitude to service policy making, whether in the form of a formal service planning system, or a set of check lists. This attitude must build on a clear understanding of the main tasks of service management, of which service planning is one.

Main tasks of service management

Service management can be resolved into a number of main tasks, as follows:

1. *Understanding the current situation and its likely evolution*

One of the starting points of service management is obtaining, analysing and assessing information. With a given set of objectives, the first task (logically, not sequentially) is to establish the current and likely future situation of the company. This means understanding the state of the company itself (profitability of particular service products, or of products, customers or areas serviced, service strengths and weaknesses along a variety of dimensions, etc.) and of the business environment (competitive behaviour, customer needs, market conditions, legal, technological, etc.). This process is the 'service audit', the aim of which is to answer the simple questions 'Where are we now, and what will happen if we continue our current policies?' Service management's task here is to establish a balance between data gathering and analytical exercises in their own right, and the use of this kind of investigation as a core part of the process of policy change.

2. *Establishing a mechanism for policy making*

There must be a mechanism for creating policy choices, evaluating them and choosing between them. This may or may not be a formal service planning process. In smaller companies, the process may be very informal. In larger companies, there may be a highly formal process. However it is done, the mechanism should be integrated (i.e. interaction between different elements of the service mix and the rest of the company should be taken into account), allow room for creativity, take account of the strengths and weaknesses of the service implementation apparatus, be realistic (not waste time considering alternatives which are unlikely to be achievable), and be as responsive as market, competitive, technological and other pressures require. It is no use having a mechanism which thoroughly evaluates all alternatives with sophisticated procedures, if it always delivers policies too late.

The service plan (if it exists) is a detailed account of environmental and company analysis, choices evaluated and made, their customer and financial consequences, etc. Having a formal plan is a useful discipline. It helps to ensure that key opportunities and risks are fully examined, key interdependencies taken into account, and implementation aspects fully investigated. It provides a common base for communication and understanding within the service function and between service and other functions. The risk with a service plan is that it becomes an extension of financial planning (providing figures via which service budgets can be set and service performance controlled) rather than a policy-making process. One sign of this is dominance of the quantitative over the qualitative or conceptual.

3. *Setting up a structure to implement service policy*

With service policy decided (whether or not formalised in a plan), a structure must be designed to implement it (though it is rarely approached in as zero-based manner as this). This means deciding organisation size, number of levels, allocation of responsibilities, spans of control, required skills and other personal attributes of staff, remuneration, incentives, motivation, communication, reporting, control/administrative systems, training and so on. In a stable business environment, there is rarely the need for substantial re-evaluation of the service organisation - change tends to be evolutionary. In unstable markets, frequent and substantial organisational change may be necessary. This is one of the most difficult tasks of service managers.

The above refers to the organisation 'system'. Once this has been decided, the system has to be made to work, by fixing targets, incentives and budgets for individuals or teams, by flexing these to the requirements of the evolving service situation, and by managing individuals and teams on a day to day basis. Finally, the results of all this effort have to be monitored against budgets.This monitoring process may generate valuable information about the costs of particular service activities and about service productivity.

THE SERVICE PROCESS

The service process can be resolved into several components, as shown in Figure 1.3. In this figure, the process starts with overall company objectives and strategies. These are combined with analysis of the environment, both internal (e.g. resources, skills, technologies) and external (e.g.competition, customer needs), to show what service objectives and strategies are appropriate. From this flow particular policies relating to the service mix (e.g. level of service, contract options, prices) and to how the service mix is to be implemented (e.g. planning process, organisation, control, motivation). All this results in service achievement. This achievement may be performance (service revenue, level of

COMPANY OBJECTIVES AND STRATEGY

FINANCIAL	MARKET PRESENCE	RESOURCES/SKILLS
Revenue/cash	Share	Production/technology
Margin/return on assets	Product strength, image	Marketing/service/finance
Asset turn	User satisfaction/loyalty	

INTERNAL AND EXTERNAL ENVIRONMENT

RESOURCES AND SKILLS	GENERAL EXTERNAL	CUSTOMERS	COMPETITION
Financial	Technology	Needs	Numbers
Production/technology	Economy	Buying power	Resources
Service skills	Legal	Behaviour	Skills
Channel presence/loyalty	Political	Use patterns	Behaviour

SERVICE OBJECTIVES AND STRATEGY

MONETARY	STANCE	CUSTOMERS	CHANNELS
Revenue/cash	Aggressive/reactive	Number/type	Own
Share	Efficient	Loyalty	Third party
Asset turn	Leader/follower	Location	Co-operation
ROA/profit/margin	Specialist	Penetration	

SERVICE POLICIES - SERVICE MIX

CUSTOMERS, MARKETS	SERVICE PRODUCTS	PRICES	PROMOTION OF SERVICE PRODUCTS	DISTRIBUTION
Number	Range	Margin	Target population	Channel choice
Value	Leadership	Flexibility	Objectives	Parts vs labour
Spread	Quality	Negotiability	Budget	Motivation
Variety	Number	Discounts	Means/media	Support
Penetration	Contract terms	Cross-subsidy	Message	Training

SERVICE POLICIES - SERVICE IMPLEMENTATION AND SUPPORT

ANALYSIS, ASSESSMENT	DECISION MAKING	PLANNING	ORGANISATION INCENTIVES	TARGETS, PRODUCTIVITY	CONTROL,
Obtain/analyse internal and external data	Create choices	Review/audit	Structure to achieve all aspects of plan	Fix group & individual targets	Control performance achievement
Prepare data for use in decisions & planning	Evaluate choices	Co-ordinate decisions	Allocate responsibility	Provide incentives to achieve	Control expenditure
	Decide on service mix	Provide framework for targets and control	Fix budgets		

ACHIEVEMENT - PERFORMANCE

REVENUE/PROFIT	MARKET SHARE	CUSTOMER CARE
Total & by area/product/client	Revenue & physical: by product, area, market, accounts, key accounts	Opinion of service and of company
Cash flow/asset turn	Number/type of clients	Level of service
Growth		
Return on assets/margin		

ACHIEVEMENT - PRODUCTIVITY

FINANCIAL	SEMI-FINANCIAL	PHYSICAL
service cost as % of revenue	Revenue per unit input (engineer, parts, etc.)	Input-output ratios (units serviced per man)
Gross or net contribution of service spend (total & per item of service mix)	Machines serviced per amount spent on service etc	Inter-input ratios (managers per man)
		Inter-output ratios (mix of products serviced)

Figure 1.3 The Service Process

service, customer care, etc.), or productivity (i.e. what it cost to achieve it). Achievement and productivity only become apparent after the event (though they will normally be forecast). This process may loop back many times in considering different policies.

Figure 1.3 also provides a checklist of the different activities that need to be put together to make the service operation work, and therefore provides a test for omissions. It gives an idea of the logical ordering of policies, and therefore a test for consistency and integration. Smaller companies may not want to devote time to considering many aspects of the diagram, but even if only once a year, it will be worth going through company service policies against the diagram, to see whether any areas which might yield additional profit or performance have been overlooked.

Objectives, strategies and constraints

Like most functions, service is required to deliver various outputs, subject to various constraints. The main output is some combination of profit and satisfied customers. In some companies (e.g. if service is a separate business, or in a third party maintenance company), the profit objective is clearly visible, with customer satisfaction seen as a way to more service profit. In other companies, customer satisfaction delivered by service is a major determinant of marketing success. No one set of objectives is absolutely right or wrong. What is important, however, is that service objectives should follow consistently from overall company objectives and strategies (e.g. development of new business, maintenance of market share, development of position as premium supplier). Often, this logic is broken. When operating conditions (e.g. equipment reliability, size of installed base, number of sites) are changing quickly, it is especially important to preserve this link.

So the service process starts with the objectives of the organisation. Prime objectives are likely to be financial (profit, revenue, cash or asset turn based) or market share based, but there may be qualitative objectives, such as product or service leadership in particular markets. Company strategy sets the main lines of how objectives are to be achieved. Service policy can only depart from these principles for very strong reasons. So, a company might decide to make its profit through concentrating on high margin, premium applications, justified by high standards of total after-sales support. Under these circumstances, a range of service products which included a cut-price, low service level contract might not be acceptable, unless specifically marketed to users with a high internal service capability.

Analysis of the internal and external environment

This aims to answer two questions:

1. What are we capable of doing (i.e. what resources and skills do we have)?
2. What is our outside environment like, and what will it want (customer) or permit (e.g. competitors, economy, technology, legislation) us to do?

Internal capabilities are assessed relative to customer needs and to the capabilities of other companies supplying your actual or potential customers. Which customers and competitors you assess depends on what you think you are capable of doing. This analysis also provides a test for the feasibility of overall objectives.

Formulating service objectives

The use of terms such as 'objective' and 'strategy' represent attempts to distinguish levels of generality in decisions. If an objective is defined as a particular goal to be reached, then the strategy would be the general way in which that goal was to be reached, policy would be the details of the methods by which the goal was to be reached, and so on. A decision at a particular level provides the framework for decisions at the next level down. Each strategy can normally be resolved into a number of strategies for different service mix elements and for service implementation. The more strategic a decision, the more substantial and long lasting are likely to be the changes in the service mix and in service implementation.

A distinction can be drawn between market presence and financial objectives or strategies. 'Market presence' relates to activity in the market (e.g. proportion of own-make machines serviced, amount of third party business attracted), while 'financial' relates to the financial implications of activity. Some strategies or objectives (e.g. target service revenue) do not fall clearly into either class. Financial targets may derive from overall company financial goals. Profit objectives may be translated into service profit targets, or margins. If significant assets are used in service (e.g. spare parts), return on assets may be a key target.

Objectives and strategies must be feasible. The commercial environment and relative strengths and weaknesses of the company determine what objectives and strategies will be feasible. So, though the logical start of analysis is with objectives, these should in turn be tested for feasibility. The feasibility of a financial objective depends on a company's competitive strength. If the company is on a par with competition in all respects, then it is unlikely over the long term to make more profit than them, unless its customers are highly insensitive to service price.

Suppose a company has been used to a service margin of 35%, but can no longer maintain it. Competitors are all making 25%. Is 35% not feasible? This depends on whether the company has advantages that competitors do not (e.g. installed base density, equipment reliability). If so, perhaps it should still make 35%, if it can match competitors' efficiency, while retaining its other advantages. Or it might have underinvested in service recently (e.g. in programmes to increase efficiency), and this has affected the margin. The underinvestment may have been due to requiring too high a margin in the past, so a temporary further dip in margin may solve the problem. It can be very counter-productive to pursue service objectives in an under-resourced manner, leading to larger falls in profit than might occur with a more realistic relation between objectives and resources. If the company is not prepared to overcome the reasons for infeasibility, then management may have to modify its overall business objectives. Their problem, of course, is to understand whether the infeasibility is real, or due to unwillingness of service management to confront difficult issues (e.g. risk, new policies, etc.).

Service objectives may reflect historical rather than current or future conditions. In a fast growing market where competition is weak, complex objectives may not be required. As growth slows, competitive and productivity pressures may increase, and objectives should relate to efficiency/performance requirements for addressing particular segments of the market.

Service objectives may include market share (overall or in particular segments), customer or segment penetration, prioritisation of particular customers, levels of service, and customer satisfaction. The process of setting objectives and evaluation for feasibility is iterative. It need not be carried out every year. But it should be adhered to as a general principle. It should include choice between different implementation paths. Only when the way in which a policy is to be implemented is examined can an objective be shown to be truly feasible or not.

Formulating service strategies

Given company objectives, there are various strategies to achieve them. One strategic classification is 'competitive stance'. An 'aggressive' stance aims to attack competition, either by taking service revenue away from it (whether through product, price or any other method), or using service as a sales tool to take market share from competition. The converse of this is a 'defensive' stance, where the main aim is to preserve existing market share or profit. Similar to this distinction is that between 'leading' and 'following' or 'reactive' stances. A leading stance may not be aggressive (though it can be). The emphasis here is on doing things which competitors are not doing.

We can distinguish 'volume' and 'specialist' service strategies. A volume stance is where a company is committed to developing service to cover as much of the eligible market as possible, compensating for standardisation (and lack of exact fit with customers' needs) by lower price or modularity in service products. The specialist or 'segmenting' approach is based on attuning the service mix closely to the needs of identified narrow market segments. This might be associated with a premium price.

There is also 'operations strategy', the general way in which the service organisation makes and implements decisions. A company may be flexible and fleet-footed, quick to react or take up opportunities, or it might be planning-intensive, good at anticipating challenges and opportunities in advance, but needing the time to rearrange resources to deal with change.

Translating service strategies into policies

The next step is to translate strategies into operating policies for different aspects of service (or, in larger companies, between different parts of the service organisation). Every objective should have clear implications for the service organisation. 'Being the top service company' does not fit this definition, while 'providing 97% uptime to certain customers' does. Of course, responsibility for delivery of objectives is not confined to the service function. In many policy areas, service shares responsibility with other functions. These include:

- Product planning, design and engineering (divided between service, marketing, R&D, engineering and product design).
- Manpower requirements (divided between service, finance and personnel).
- Service cash flow (divided between service, marketing and finance).
- Parts inventory levels (divided between service, finance, production and physical distribution).

Whatever looks best in principle, the nature of the division depends on the business environment, on the particular managers in charge of different areas, and the way in which they are rewarded or assessed. If parts inventory is the responsibility of the distribution function, and the distribution manager is rewarded if he keeps inventory down, then severe problems of stock-outs can occur. On the other hand, if he is rewarded by profits, and if he understands the importance of live inventory, these problems are unlikely to arise. So, the solution is to ensure that, whatever the formal division of responsibility, the control, motivation and communication system works to produce the best result for overall company objectives.

Operating policies need to be specified in terms similar to the following:

1. Which products shall be serviced (own, other make - box or components).
2. To what standards (uptime, response time, performance standards).
3. With what prices, contract terms.
4. At what profit.
5. Over what time period.
6. In what markets, segments and locations.
7. With what marketing support.
8. With what service organisation.
9. With what implementation, motivation and control procedures.
10. With what productivity/service cost.

For each of these, a service plan should be able to give justification in terms of operational service objectives. If service objectives are ill-formed or only specified very generally, this is difficult to do, and customers' demand for service is unlikely to be dealt with competently.

CHECKLIST FOR CHAPTER 1

This chapter introduces all the topics covered in the book. A full checklist for this chapter would duplicate other checklists, so this checklist concentrates on the overall approach rather than details.

Staff situation

* Are our service staff motivated to deliver customer satisfaction?
* Have they been trained to deliver customer satisfaction?
* Are our staff involved enough in decisions which affect them to be seriously interested in creating satisfied customers?
* Do our managers relate to their staff as we want our staff to relate to customers?
* Are the criteria on which we assess staff related to customer satisfaction?
* Does the way in which we have functionalised the business handicap efforts to increase customer satisfaction? If so, what are we doing to mitigate this effect?

Understanding customers' attitudes to service

* Do we attempt to segment the market for service, to enable us to deliver better service to particular groups of customers?
* How do our customers perceive us as suppliers of service? Do they distinguish the technical service they receive from other aspects of our relationship with them? If so, how?
* What determines our customers' perceptions of us as suppliers of technical service? As providers of customer satisfaction?

Service policy process

* Do we have a policy process which enables us to take the right decisions at the right times and implement them correctly? Does it avoid bureaucracy? Is the process responsive to change in the business and technical environment?
* Are appropriate aspects of our service policy process communicated to and well understood by all those involved in delivering service?
* Does our service policy process allow room for creativity in generating different policy alternatives?

* Do we analyse the market context in which we are providing service often enough (demand for service, competitive behaviour, profitability of particular service products, areas, our strengths relative to competition, general economic factors, etc.)?
* Do we review our policy process against this market context, to see whether the process is likely to remain appropriate if the market context is changing?

Service objectives
* Are our service objectives clearly specified?
* Do our objectives take into account longer term company needs (market share, customer loyalty, general after-market profit, etc.)?
* Have we tested our service objectives for feasibility?
* Do the objectives relate clearly to our perceived strengths and weaknesses, as a service organisation and as a company?
* Do our objectives match the objectives of other functions with which service interacts (marketing, production, design, finance)?

Service mix
* Do we recognise the variety of service mix options that are available, particularly in relation to policies on customer satisfaction, product, price and promotion?
* Do we have a good mechanism for choosing between different options?
* Does this mechanism include appropriate input from other functions?

Implementation of service policy
* Is our service organisation clearly structured, staffed, managed, motivated and controlled to deliver the combination of financial and customer satisfaction objectives specified in our company business plan?
* Do the targets and controls by which we manage staff in the service organisation relate clearly to our customer satisfaction and financial objectives?
* Does the data returning via our control processes give us a clear idea of how we can improve performance?
* Does our service organisation's productivity ensure that financial objectives are met? What are we doing to improve service productivity?

2 THE DEMAND FOR SERVICE

In examining the demand for service, we need to answer these questions:

1. Who are or should be our customers?
2. What are their perceptions and requirements of the service marketing mix?

Developing a customer-oriented perspective

In a service business, company success depends on the ability to see the situation from the perspective of the customer. This perspective is sometimes difficult for professional marketing people to maintain, given the internal pressures of running a company, so it is not surprising if service management finds it difficult. However, it is important to achieve it, as service is part of a process by which a company achieves objectives via its relationships with its customers, whose view of the service process may differ from the supplier's. Some companies lose sight of this.

Service is not just the provision of technical service in exchange for money (Figure 2.1). It is an exchange of value - the supplier provides value (i.e. something that helps meet objectives) to the customer, who returns value to the supplier (Figure 2.2). Further, the value supplied by the supplier may not be the same as that perceived by the customer. The supplier may reckon it in physical or technical terms, e.g. response time or uptime. The customer may reckon it in terms of equipment output or a feeling of confidence that equipment will be available when needed. Consider the value returned by the customer. Does the customer know the price that he has paid? Does he perceive price as the main cost, or the costs incurred by failure? 'User costs' may dwarf service costs. Is the receiver of the service the one perceived by the supplier? Is it the equipment operator, the departmental head, or the purchasing authority? Is the supplier of the service the one perceived by the customer? The perceived supplier may be the engineer, not the company. We therefore need to redraw our picture (Figure 2.3). Suppliers invite problems because they only see the left hand side of the picture. But a picture which is based on the right hand side only may get the supplier into trouble for other reasons (e.g. costs).

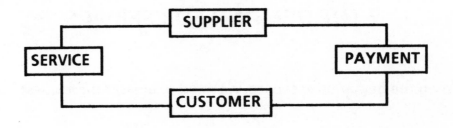

Figure 2.1 Simple view of customer/supplier relationship

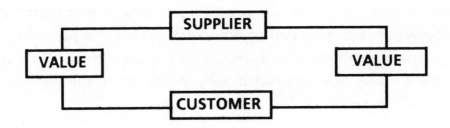

Figure 2.2 More complex view of customer/supplier relationship

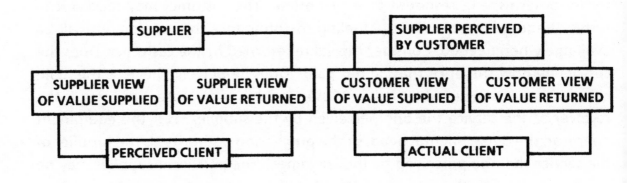

Figure 2.3 Different perceptions of the relationship

Customer perceptions of suppliers

Many customers see suppliers as being more concerned with products and technology than with the customer. Even suppliers who avoid this run the risk of orientation to the needs of historic rather than current customers. Suppliers used to dealing with large customers may not adjust well to the needs of smaller customers. Suppliers used to dealing with the public sector may not understand private sector customers' needs.

Some suppliers make little attempt to communicate with customers, except when it comes to selling them equipment. More positive messages relate to depth of understanding of customer service needs and commitment to support. Most customers tend to look for evidence of long-term commitment, continuity and stability. The supplier's desire to establish a deep, long lasting connection with the customer rings false against a background of failure to communicate more basic, day-to-day matters. Perceptions of service depend on the overall nature of communication between supplier and customer.

Supplier evaluation procedures

The reason for stressing these points is that many customers buy the company, not the product or service. Suppliers must find out their customers' supplier-evaluation criteria, to establish how to present service to them. These criteria may be embodied in a formal rating system, where each factor is weighted by its importance to the customer, and each supplier scored according to his performance on each factor. Here are some of the factors used:
- General reputation.
- Degree of understanding of needs.
- Personal relationships.
- Technical excellence.
- Product quality.
- Reliability of new product launch dates.
- Breadth and compatibility of product line.
- Availability of third party after-market products.
- Availability of compatible equipment from third parties.
- Financial options.
- General price level.
- Responsiveness to customer needs (speed and quality).
- Sales force quality.

- Prompt delivery.
- Documentation.
- After-sales service.
- After-sales support.

Formal systems tend to be used by customers with central purchasing authority. Informal systems may be used by other members of the 'buying centre'. The same criteria may be applied to distributors, with the additional factor of strength of connection between supplier and distributor.

ORGANISATIONAL PURCHASING

To understand customer needs, we need to understand how organisations buy. The difference between organisational and consumer buying is not as clear cut as often supposed. Organisational buyers do try to achieve some level of rationality in their purchasing objectives, search for suppliers and solutions, and negotiation, but their prejudices and emotions influence how they go through the purchasing process. The major differences are ones of degree rather than kind. Organisational purchases tend to formally involve more people (though family purchases can be seen as organisational purchases), with more formal differentiation of roles (e.g. buyer, user, influencer, gatekeeper - see below). Organisations may impose policies and procedures on buyers. These require proposals, quotations, terms, conditions and contracts. The objective of purchasing can normally be traced to a particular business, departmental or other objective.

The buying centre

In many cases, the customer for service is not an individual, but an establishment or organisation, within which a number of individuals may influence attitudes and decisions in relation to service. We need to understand how different individuals contribute to decisions, what is the nature and extent of their influence, and what criteria or rules each will apply in bringing their influence to bear. The main roles are:

Users of the product or service. They may play many other roles as well.

Initiators, who initiate the purchasing process.

Influencers, who in any way influence purchases, via policy or consultation.

Buyers, who have authority to place orders. They typically play an important role in deciding specifications and negotiating.

Deciders, who have the power to make the decision, via formal authority, strong informal power due to position within organisation, or personal links. In routine buying, the buyers are often the deciders.

Gatekeepers, who affect relevant information flows (e.g. aware users, researchers, purchasing agents, secretaries, switchboard operators).

Each one of these categories may operate with very different decision criteria, and be susceptible to influence in very different ways.

Buyphases

In acquiring a service product, an organisation may go through some of the following stages, or 'buyphases'. These are defined as follows:

Problem recognition: anticipation or recognition of problem/need and of general solution. This often takes place when change occurs in the buying organisation, when it is exposed to promotional influence, or when an existing service turns out to be unsatisfactory. Problem recognition can be stimulated by appropriate marketing actions (e.g. promotion of a new service product).

General need description: General characteristics of needed service(s). For standard services (e.g. standard maintenance contracts), this is easy. For others (e.g. total on-site maintenance), it may involve intensive work with technical staff, users and others. The supplier can often help customers to define their needs more precisely.

Product specification: Detailed characteristics of service to be provided.

Supplier search: Search for and qualification of sources. In many cases, this search will not go further than the supplier of the equipment. For frequently acquired types of after-sale item (e.g. parts, supplies), the buyer may have an established supplier list. For some services, the search may be renewed periodically (e.g. on contract renewal). The resulting list will be edited to a qualified list. Suppliers who do not make the effort to establish themselves as prime suppliers will tend to be edited out often.

Proposal solicitation: Acquisition and analysis of proposal from qualified suppliers. Proposal writing and presentation skills are crucial if the supplier is to do himself justice at this stage.

Supplier selection: Evaluation of proposals and selection of supplier, on factors such as those listed earlier, perhaps using a formal supplier evaluation model. Even if a supplier is rated number one, it does not imply he will get all the business, since some customers prefer to spread orders.

Order routine specification: Specifying an ordering routine.

Performance review: Performance feedback and evaluation, via formal or informal evaluation of users' satisfaction with the service.

The buygrid

Buying centre behaviour varies according to the nature of the purchase in question. Three "buyclasses" are usually distinguished, as follows:

New task: The organisation has no experience of the type of service (typically for service for a newly purchased item of equipment for a totally new use within the organisation). The greater the cost or risk, the larger the number of individuals in the buying centre, and the greater their information seeking. This kind of decision provides the supplier with a challenge and an opportunity. It has to reach as many people in the buying centre as possible with the correct message, information and assistance at the correct time.

Straight rebuy: The buyer reorders without modification (e.g. renewal of a service contract). This may be handled routinely by the purchasing department, depending on satisfaction with the existing arrangement. Existing suppliers try to maintain quality and service to keep other suppliers out, while competitors exploit any source of dissatisfaction to get the business.

Modified rebuy: The buyer seeks to change supplier, contract specifications, prices, or terms, but requires the same service. This may be triggered by awareness of the availability of a new approach to service to satisfy the same need, and puts more pressure on existing suppliers. This situation may be seen to be very risky by the buyer, since users and other members of the buying centre may have firm expectations based upon past experience.

'Buyclasses' are not comprehensive definitions, but illustrate three possible positions on a continuum from 'no change' to 'all change'. They help in focusing attention on key marketing tasks (e.g. what, to whom, when). Not all buyphases are gone through for all decisions. In the new task situation, all the stages might operate. For modified or straight rebuy, some stages might be modified or compressed. Other stages may be identifiable. The stages also vary considerably in their degree of formality.

Influences in organisational purchasing

These can be classified as follows:

Business environment: Political, economic (e.g. production, trade), financial (e.g. interest rates, credit), legal and technical (e.g. obsolescence)

24

Organisation influences: Structure, culture and style of the organisation, e.g. degree of centralisation or formality of purchasing decisions (e.g. approval authority), allocation of responsibilities for performance and quality, influence of different members of buying centre, how these members form their attitudes, use of formal supplier and service evaluation processes.

Purchasing environment: Type of service that is being bought, type of task, relative offerings (price, quality, terms, etc.) of different suppliers, experience of different members of the buying centre of service and suppliers, intensity of need, effect of marketing mix of suppliers (e.g. promotion).

These influences, together with an understanding of the composition of the buying centre, buyphases and buygrid for each customer, provide a check list for research and information gathering.

Organisational purchasing - a computing example

With technical progress and the increased diffusion of computing in the organisation, computer service needs are changing. For example, the number of local and remote connections to end-user departments is growing quickly. This means that end-user support will have to be considerably expanded as more staff become direct users. Distributed printing and memory devices will produce a surge in the demand for maintenance, until reliability improves. These trends have a major impact on service policy. Engineers will have a much larger number of individual customers within the organisation (unless the customer uses in-house service). Alternatively, the approach of supplying reserve equipment may prove to be much more viable. The end-user may have a very different set of uptime requirements than the data processing manager. The DP department may find it increasingly difficult to retain centralised responsibility for maintenance.

SERVICE MARKET SIZE

In some companies, the market opportunity for service is outside the control of service management (e.g. the installed base provided by sales, with service contracts sold by salesmen). Service may be tasked to respond only to certain user requirements. In some companies (especially the more profit oriented ones), this attitude is changing, and companies are looking at the definition of the service market from a fresh perspective.

Service market size can be measured in several ways, from service revenue, through number of buyers or users of service products, to the number of times service products are used. Each measure forms part of the following identity:

Service revenue = Number of customers x number of machines per customer x number of service calls per machine x company share of calls x actual or imputed revenue per call x proportion of revenue billed and obtained.

Similar identities can be written for service cost and profit. Such identities may help to establish when a new policy is needed. You may be trying to get 100% share of calls when it is easier to increase revenue per call via high priced, high level of service contracts. So, the measure used depends on policy. For example, if you have two service products (e.g. an emergency service for essential equipment, and a long response time for non-essential equipment, or products X and Y), you might use any of the following measures:
  - Value of X and Y demanded and sold, overall and per machine.
  - Number of customers for X or Y or both, for different types of equipment.
  - Number of times per year X or Y or both are used by customers.
  - Mean, median or modal value of products bought per customer.

These measures may be in terms of market segment (e.g. machine type, new users, geography, industry sector, customer size, etc.) or market share. If you aim to increase sales of X by promoting it to customers who need faster service, you need to measure how many more of these customers you attract, and what value of service is supplied to them. You may increase the number of users of this service, but find that the value (cost) of service supplied is in excess of the extra revenue obtained, because you have attracted the most demanding customers. You may therefore need to use several measures at once.

SEGMENTING THE SERVICE MARKET

A segment is part of the market which differs from the rest of the market. Markets are not uniform, but consist of many potential customers, who differ in their needs, how they can be accessed, willingness to pay certain prices, and so on. They can be grouped into segments, each composed of potential buyers sharing certain characteristics. Each segment is defined by a number of dimensions (e.g. industry, geography, application, language, culture, buying pattern). Though segments can be defined with definite boundaries, we often operate with overlapping segments. Further, many dimensions of segmentation are continuous variables (e.g. size of establishment), so the dividing line between segments is arbitrary. We could specify the typical member of a segment, but most members will be atypical - few segment members are average.

A segment is not necessarily a distinct sub-group. A given customer may belong to two segments of the same market. He may be in the market for rapid service for some equipment or some sites, and not for other equipment or sites. Individual segments can be measured in as many ways as the total market.

Reasons for segmenting
There are three main reasons for segmenting:

1. It may give a better basis for predicting total market behaviour, by aggregating behaviour of different segments.
2. If segments of the market are known to respond differently to service policy, and if policies can be devised which vary in their effect on segments, this may enhance achievement of service objectives.
3. Segmented policy can bring advantages of specialisation and concentration of resources. These advantages may be absolute, in the sense that better performance or lower costs result (the simplest case of this is geographical segmentation, which the economics of service often dictate). They may also be competitive, in the sense that successful segmentation precludes options for the competition. This of course may be offset by the diseconomies that are sometimes inherent in dedicating resources, policy, etc., to particular parts of the market. These points apply to the overall service effort and to individual items of the mix. It is possible to define which variables are more likely to lend themselves to segmenting, and which not, according to the advantages of specialisation and concentration, versus those of non-specialisation.

The bases for segmentation include:
Geographical
Segments are defined by customer location (national, rural/suburban/city). Segmenting by country tends to be used at the highest strategic level. Thus, giving some countries priority in the international launch of a new service product (e.g. remote diagnostics) may be more profitable, because those countries yield higher price levels, or are less expensive to deal with. Rural/suburban/city segmentation is often used as a surrogate for density of

installed base. Remote areas may be identified as those where some elements of service will need to be subcontracted.

Purchasing power
This may be defined in a number of ways e.g. income, assets, cash. The aim is to identify customers who are most likely to buy premium service products.

Innovativeness as a buyer
This may be used as a basis for deciding whether a particular buyer is likely to want to pioneer a new form of service.

Price sensitivity
In marketing a premium service product, the ideal is to find customers who are insensitive to price. This depends on factors such as:
- The use situation (e.g. strength of benefit).
- The purchasing situation (e.g. presence of competitive suppliers).
- Price awareness and extent of effort made to get price comparisons.
- Evaluation procedures.

Many customers are less price sensitive than suppliers perceive them to be. Suppliers resort to price reductions first rather than last in trying to get business. It is not difficult to identify which customers are price-sensitive (e.g. via market research or study of their behaviour). If resources are limited, they should be concentrated on customers known to be less price sensitive (provided the supplier can meet the level of service requirements to which these customers <u>are</u> sensitive). Price may be interpreted as cost of ownership, and sensitivity may relate to total user cost of the process of which the equipment is a part.

Existing user of product class
It is usual to distinguish between first purchase (new buy) and straight and modified rebuys (or finer distinctions according to the degree of modification of the rebuy). Buyer behaviour differs between these cases, but not always predictably. Much may depend on how long the buyer has had the equipment, what his experience has been with it, and who supplied it. The sales process for straight rebuyers may need to focus on the competitive strengths of the service being offered, as the buyer may have developed benchmarks for rating competitive offerings. New buyers may need help with establishing benchmarks.

Existing user of supplier's products

If the supplier has looked after the customer, loyalty should predispose him to at least consider that supplier's service. If the supplier has failed to do this, this segmentation is still useful for deciding which customers to avoid or which will need the greatest sales effort.

Use situation, applications, benefits

This covers various topics, including:
- The tasks the equipment is used for.
- Other products with which it is used.
- The benefits it delivers to the customer.

Industry/sector

Service requirements may differ in different industries. This may be a surrogate for use situation segmentation.

Preferences and needs

This relates to factors such as:
- The need to specify service in detail or willingness to compromise by buying a standard contract.
- Level of engineer skill required.
- Frequency/timing of service requirement (independent of technical need).

Following a segmented service policy

If policy is segmented, the segments should have these characteristics.

Stability

Segments should be relatively stable. The factors that differentiate them should be understood, and not likely to disappear tomorrow.

No risk of undermining

The segment should not be likely to be undermined by competitors following a non-segmented policy. Segmentation can mean foregoing economies of scale. A specialised service force may result in more engineer waiting time, and higher administrative costs), and charging a higher price for a product that is better attuned to the need of that segment. If a competitor comes along with a service concept which is versatile enough to meet the needs of many such segments, he may be able to undercut substantially on price, and give better value to the buyer. If he is a good marketer, he may segment his advertising and promotion, to ensure that the message is got across in a focused way.

Ability to respond to segment needs

The company must be able to respond to the needs of the identified segments. Some companies cannot attune their policies and organisation to the needs of a particular segment, because skills are lacking, the organisation is inflexible or resistant to change, or because the costs of change are too high.

Availability of information

If segmentation is based on detailed understanding of customers, the information required should be available when and where it is needed.

SPECIFIC ASPECTS OF SERVICE DEMAND

We now examine certain aspects of service demand in more detail.

Effect of type of use

The consequences of failure may depend upon whether the equipment is used in connection with staff rather than line activities. In staff work, delay may be less serious. In line activities (e.g. factory automation equipment), the costs of failure can be very high. In staff activities, equipment failure may cause some of the organisation to mark time, because the organisation is not flexible enough to allocate other tasks at short notice. The equipment may be used by a unit within the organisation for which it is crucial to have a smooth relationship with the rest of the organisation, with obligations fully met, and no excuses for delay. These factors may be sensed by the engineer and could be formalised into some sort of prioritisation.

User dependence

A related aspect is user dependence. The only catering machine, word processor or computer in a small establishment may create more dependence than similar equipment in larger establishments. While out-house services may be used to perform the tasks for which the equipment is required, the penalty in terms of cost and inconvenience may be high. Uptime requirements may be at their most extreme where there is no alternative equipment.

One way to analyse the above factors is via the effect of failure or substandard performance on the use of complementary and substitutional inputs (e.g. labour, other equipment). For complementary inputs, key questions relate to effects on costs when these inputs are unable to perform because of downtime. For substitutional inputs, key questions concern trueness of substitution, availability of substitutes (e.g. back-up equipment, out-house services, manual labour), and the speed and cost of substitution.

Value factors
The value of service to the customer is closely related to dependence. The payment made for service may be just the minimum value to the customer. Suppliers who offer only one level of service on a particular machine lose the chance of capitalising on intensity of demand for service via higher priced options, but also risk having more dissatisfied customers through not discriminating between intense and less intense need.

Related to this is the total cost and value to the user of obtaining equipment services, and the relative importance of the machine/service cost component. In cases of high dependence and where equipment cost is a low proportion of total cost and value, the best solution may be to sell back-up or fail-safe equipment rather than try to meet user needs by fast service. The design, pricing and marketing of fail-safe or back-up equipment needs to be integrated with service product and pricing policy, taking into account the value and user costs of using substitute equipment.

There may be a difference between perceived and actual costs. An objective estimate of the costs to the customer of equipment being unavailable may not accord with the 'subjective costs' of individuals who are affected by this. This should be taken into account in devising cost justification arguments for pricing and terms of service.

ATTITUDES TOWARDS UPTIME
Customer perceptions of service may be dominated by a factor which service does not control - equipment reliability. With design and manufacturing having prime responsibility, and sales an additional responsibility for placing equipment in uses where its level of reliability is least likely to cause problems, this can be frustrating for service staff.

Downtime may be defined as anything from complete failure to substandard operation. Downtime may affect a whole system or individual components of it (leaving some parts working). In some cases, it may be due to hardware, in others software. Sophisticated users may have procedures for dealing with substandard operation or partial failure, while for others it may amount to total failure. Attitudes may depend on the tasks the equipment is carrying out when it fails. As equipment ages, users may expect it to fail more frequently, and not expect to receive the same level of service as when the equipment was new. A history of inadequate service may condition users to a low level of service (particularly if they do not have similar equipment being serviced by more effective suppliers), but improving the level of service may be crucial if competition is intensifying.

Faulty design or assembly may be distinguished by users as causes of failure. Sophisticated users may demand 'field fixing', and seek alternative solutions when the equipment is due for replacement or when additional equipment is required. Comments made by field engineers to absolve themselves of responsibility for failure may do a lot of damage to marketing prospects.

Customer causes of downtime

The customer may be at 'fault' when problems occur. This message should be delivered very gently. There may be simple abuse - not following correct operating procedures. But if operating procedures are very complex, thought should be given to redesign, customer training or marketing policies (the equipment may be being sold to 'unsuitable' users). Warning signs include particular kinds of customers consistently reporting the same fault. Sometimes, the buying decision may have been based on an incorrect assumption of a particular level of skill or equipment- dedication of customer staff. Overuse is a different problem. The equipment may have been sold for uses where the workload is too great for the equipment, or the buyer may be attempting to economise by buying equipment of too low capacity. Either case represents a real risk of total loss of business to the supplier.

Definition of reliability

The first step in analysing attitudes to reliability is to understand what definition(s) of reliability a user operates with. Suppliers who track the usage level of their equipment (e.g. for debiting purposes) often assume that users define reliability as failure per amount of usage. The users' definition is often in terms of failure frequency (total, partial, or at critical times), or the inverse of these, uptime. This may be because the customer needs equipment availability as much as a particular volume of throughput.

Perceived reliability

The impact of any 'objective' failure rate on customer satisfaction depends on various factors, which include perceived experience with previous or similar equipment. Users accustomed to high total uptime proportions with frequent substandard operation may be dissatisfied with equipment with slightly lower uptime proportions, even though operation is always perfect. Other aspects of the level of service (e.g. response time, engineer skills, time to repair) often affect perceived reliability, though this relationship is normally stronger the other way round - users of reliable machines are generous in their perceptions of service, while high levels of service may not have quite the same effect on perceived reliability.

Promises of high reliability can cut two ways. Users with acute reliability needs will be attracted to products which are sold on reliability, so service standards may have to be raised for that equipment (and the converse applies to products which are not sold on reliability). However, users who have been convinced that their equipment is more reliable may tolerate lower standards if they were responsible for acquisition, in order to save face.

Reliability requirements

To decide whether to use preventive maintenance and other ways of reducing downtime, suppliers may ask users about their band of tolerance of reliability levels (e.g. minimum required versus expected levels). Responses tend to be crude averages, and usually affected by other aspects of the level of service. Conditional questions ('what would be?') are a notorious trap in any market research, tending to produce wish lists, or unreasonably high or tolerant demands, especially if users are asked to value particular reliability levels. There are problems of recall concerning the situation at the time of failure, and also problems of post-rationalisation. It is better to research actual occurrences of failure, not long after they occur, though this must be handled more sensitively than general questions about reliability. These points also apply to all other aspects of the level of service.

ATTITUDES TO RESPONSE TIME

Many customers do not use response time measures to evaluate service. Some customers operate with downtime measures, and when asked about response time, have to deduce what they thought response time was from a perceived downtime. Even if all customers measured response time, their measure might not coincide with that of the suppliers. Response time perceptions are very elastic. They may be exaggerated by low reliability or by variability in response time (customers may remember the worst) or reduced by quick diagnosis and repair or good customer- engineer relations. Fine-tuning response time to affect customer perceptions of it is not always appropriate. Selective memory and rationalisation are frequent. The solution may be to research near to the time of occurrence, to produce a focus on a specific incident, though remember that it is the *lasting* perception that counts in contract renewal.

Customers' perceptions may be in terms of blocks of time, divided by key events (e.g. meal breaks, number of peak load periods lost). Required response times may be phrased in terms of these blocks, such as morning call - afternoon service, or afternoon call - next morning service.

Companies that research service needs often only use the above kind of data to formulate service policy, instead of returning the data to the sales operation to improve selling of equipment or service contracts. This parallels the failure of data on the use situation to flow from sales to service.

ATTITUDES TO SERVICE PRICING

Suppliers' pricing research is often weak, making it hard to check how different customers respond to price. The responsiveness that service management is interested in is of two kinds - relative to other elements of service, and responsiveness to price (and other service) differentials with competitors. Even if information is of low quality, it is important to classify customers by their trade-offs between price and other aspects of service. It may be difficult or expensive to identify these groups accurately, so it may be better to test the responsiveness of different groups by policy changes or examination of existing purchasing behaviour. If research is carried out, the basis for it might be stated preferences between service products at different price levels, though this is not usually a reliable guide. It might be via questionnaires to establish perceptions of and attitudes to the service of the company and its competitors.

Price awareness

This analysis must take into account degree of awareness of level of service. Some buyers are not very conscious of the price they pay for service, the prices charged by competitors, the benefits of one or other service product, and so on. Service management often assumes that customers are as well informed as they are themselves, or care as much as they do about choice between service products. Reasons for lack of price awareness include complexity of pricing (especially for periodic payments or prices bundled with equipment prices) or outdating of price information. If there is known to be a lack of price awareness in certain customers, this may be a good basis for price discrimination (depending on competitive conditions).

Customers may be more aware of or sensitive to some elements of price than others. They may be more aware of initial purchase price than service price, more aware of big-ticket than small- ticket service prices. Suppliers of a wide range of service products often lose opportunities of increasing prices on certain items in the range because they price each product by the same rules. Capitalising on all opportunities for gaining high prices in situations of less sensitivity to price compensates for having to reduce margins on products where there is no avoiding head to head service competition.

Pricing for individual customers

The same principle applies to pricing for individual customers. The first step is to ensure that the costs of servicing particular customers are known. This does not apply to every customer. Most companies' customers follow the 80:20 rule on distribution of revenue or profitability, so it is worth looking at the costs of servicing, say, individual customers or groups of customers (usually segmented) responsible for more than a certain proportion of company revenue/profit (say 5%). The groups of customers should be segmented according to the company's own service processes. If these are geographically organised, this means examining costs of servicing particular areas. If service is organised to deal with particular kinds of customer, so much the better.

Analysing cost variations by customer is a step which companies often fail to take, relying instead on average costs in reckoning the profitability of servicing particular customers or groups of customers. The average costs used may be average variable costs or average total costs (i.e. including overhead). The impact of this approach on profit depends on market conditions. In competitive conditions, where the company has little control over price, business that is not profitable may be taken on, or business that would be profitable may not. If conditions are less competitive, then the company may be undercharging some customers, and overcharging others, risking attracting too many unprofitable customers, and losing profitable customers.

If the cost of servicing a particular customer is known, then some of it may be chargeable to him, especially if he is less sensitive to charges where he can see some logic in the premium. Examples of this include special parts storage, administration, communication, and customisation. A whole price strategy can be based on this principle, by gaining a position in new customers by a low price, and then building up charges as the relationship develops. The best way to do this is by ensuring that the charges actually correspond to additional services. Diagnosis of the need for these services will often only be possible once a service relationship exists with the customer. In other circumstances, there may be no corresponding value added - charging additional sums effectively depends on 'tying the customer up'.

ATTITUDES TO PRODUCTS

As new modes of technical service evolve (remote diagnosis, board replacement) changes may be required in the way customers' service needs are looked at. With remote diagnosis and (sometimes) remote repair, the fact that technical problems are solved with almost no downtime may need to be impressed upon the customer. If remote diagnosis is possible, but not remote repair, training may be needed to enable members of the customer's staff to carry out the repair (e.g. board replacement). Diagnosis may be local, but by the customer. In either of these cases, the supplier's role is to ensure that repair actions are taken and that the local parts stock is replenished. New service products will evolve, so it is important to establish customer attitudes to them.

The distinction between emergency, standard, preventive service and site engineer can be complicated by combinations of these modes, for particular time periods, machines or sites. Back-up equipment will become commoner as hardware costs fall, while customer parts inventories may be used to reduce travel and broken calls due to parts wait. Products may vary by contractual terms and pricing. These variations in product elicit different responses from customers, who may have limited experience of different products, partly because the sales force has not grasped the opportunity of obtaining additional revenue by meeting customers' service needs more exactly.

Researching product acceptability has the same traps as researching response time or reliability needs. If you ask about perceptions of or intentions to buy something the customer has not experienced, or about something not of concern to him when the question is asked, his response may not bear much relation to how he would react to the product if it were available. Recent problems with one mode of service (e.g. due to failure at a critical time) may represent good opportunities for selling up the service range. Test marketing is one way of checking the viability of this policy.

ATTITUDES TO TEETHING PROBLEMS

A newly installed piece of equipment is similar to a new product. If the equipment performs to exactly the promised reliability standard or to the same standard as the equipment it replaced, there is little need for special service actions. If there are teething problems, initial experiences can condition users' feelings towards the equipment for some time (sometimes long enough to affect the next purchase!). For this reason, equipment which is known to under-perform immediately after installation needs special service marketing treatment - a sort of preventive maintenance on the service product. Aside from the obvious technical fact of the engineer being needed, there is a lot that can be done to ensure that the initial period is painless. Higher engineer resourcing, more frequent preventive work (if appropriate) or stand-by equipment are ways of reducing the effect of teething problems. If a new machine replaces an older one sold by the same supplier, it may be appropriate to allow an overlap (although this incurs additional costs, if teething problems are severe, it might be justified).

ATTITUDES TO SERVICE SOURCE

This should be researched for pricing (strength of preference may indicate the premium that can be charged) and for general policy (e.g. preservation of service as a source of profit). The choice available to users ranges from the equipment manufacturer or distributor, a recommended (official) service agency, in-house service, and third party service. Key factors here are:

1. Perception of availability, reliability, responsiveness, cost and quality of all sources of service.
2. Use by supplier of contract terms to defend against third party service.
3. Degree of maturity of use and user for the equipment. The user who has been using a particular type of equipment and/or the particular item in question for a long time is more likely to be certain of what is involved in using alternative sources of service.

Switches of loyalty are difficult to predict. Causes range from dissatisfaction with one incident, to cost pressures. Research on this topic should avoid making respondents aware of other sources of service.

ATTITUDES TO SERVICE INTERFACE

This covers more formal aspects, such as ease of contact, complaints procedures, billing arrangements, and less formal aspects, such as preference for particular engineers, engineer attitudes and work styles. Asking the customer vague questions, may produce a 'wish list' of factors, none of them crucial. These factors may be managed better by 'tails management', where only extreme cases are dealt with. One way is to use formal complaints as a review process, rather than relying on research. This is best where there is known to be a problem. After dealing with customers who feel so strongly that they have registered a formal complaint, the next step is to find those customers who feel strongly but have not yet registered a complaint.

The individual dealing with the supplier on service may also deal with him on sales and administration. The service interface may not be distinguishable from other interfaces. This can be tested by running questionnaires on attitudes to different aspects of the interface, and testing correlation between them. Such a test might show, for example, that although the attitude to sales staff was not as positive as to service staff, the two attitudes were highly correlated across different individuals, implying that success in one area may pay off in another (and ditto for failures!).

ATTITUDES TO CONTRACTUAL SERVICE

Most suppliers prefer to have a high proportion of users on contract, because this provides a steady cash flow, is administratively more convenient, and may protect against third party maintenance. Preference for contractual service should not lead to discrimination against non-contractual customers. Both kinds of service should be marketed, recognising the advantages of each. For smaller equipment or smaller customers, the non- contractual option may be attractive (e.g. to maintain small business cash flow), especially since insurance companies offer ways of covering the risks of not having a contract. However, many customers prefer contracts only because they know that non- contractual customers receive a lower level of service.

Non-contractual service can be profitable, as domestic electrical equipment retailers and suppliers have shown. They achieve this via efficiency in administration and collection of charges or invoicing (often by engineers), and appropriate parts and labour pricing. The challenge is to find ways of meeting non-contractual customers' needs profitably. This does not preclude strong marketing of contractual service (if it really is more profitable than a well-run non-contractual operation). The administrative systems of many suppliers are not well adapted to handling occasional customers or infrequent and irregular billings of small amounts, leading to high cost and low profit for non-contractual service. If the demand for non-contractual service is great, the first step may be to revise administrative systems to ensure their capability to deal with infrequent and irregular billing.

DEMAND FOR OPERATOR TRAINING

Operator training can be an important part of the service mix, of benefit both to the user and the supplier. To the user, it means that some causes of downtime and sub-standard working can be resolved without needing to call for service, while to the supplier it can reduce the frequency of equipment maltreatment, as well as reducing the need to make a service call when equipment does malfunction. The customer's demand for training depends upon:

1. Actual and perceived complexity of equipment operation and maintenance
2. Criticality of the equipment - if it is possible to keep it going by user staff working on it, then this may be a preferred solution by the user.
3. Costs to the user of operation, sub-standard operation and downtime.
4. Operator or user turnover - a high rate can increase the chance of maltreatment, but it also increases the cost of training. If training is seen as a source of profit, this may be an opportunity for the supplier.
5. Frequency and importance of user updates (changes in equipment mix, retrofits, new machine capabilities and complexities).
6. Time available for training (flexibility, user willingness to bear cost).

CHECKLIST FOR CHAPTER 2

Value exchange and the buying centre

* What values are exchanged between our company and our customers - in general and particularly in relation to service? How may our perceptions of that value differ from that of our customers?
* Who do we think are the receivers of the service we provide - users, operators, buyers, owners, etc?
* Does our view as to who are the receivers of service correspond with that of our customers?
* Do we fully understand the composition and behaviour of our customers' buying centre, in relation to products and service?
* Do we know what influences our customers' buying centre's choices, and how these centres behave with respect to different kinds of purchase?
* How does our communication with customers convey the value we are delivering to them?
* How do our customers evaluate us (the company, our products and the service we use)? What criteria are used, and how do we rate against other providers of service?

The market for service

* What is the total market opportunity for our service operation?
* Does our definition of market opportunity take into account all the different ways in which we can supply service to our existing customers, and all the customers we might be able to supply service to if we had the right service products and marketed them appropriately?
* Do we consider the market for our service products in terms of segments, to improve our understanding of the market, to design different service products for different segments, and to take advantage of any benefits that specialisation and concentration of resources can bring us in serving the needs of particular segments?

Specific aspects of the demand for service

* Do we know how equipment usage patterns affect the value of service?
* How do our customers define reliability, uptime, downtime and its components (response time, repair time, etc.)?

* How important are reliability, uptime, downtime and its components to our customers?
* What relation do our customers' perceptions of these factors bear to the actual situation?
* What factors influence our customers' perception of these factors, and their needs and tolerances with respect to them?
* How accurately do our customers perceive the price they pay for service?
* Would our customers be willing to pay any more than they are currently paying for service, and if so, under what conditions?
* Do our customers feel any elements of our service are overpriced?
* How far is the price that our customers are willing to pay a result of successful marketing and selling of service?
* Do we optimise opportunities for price discrimination between customers?
* Are our customers aware of all the service products we could offer them?
* What are our customers' attitudes to different service products?
* Are we matching the service product mix to the needs of our customers so as to yield maximum customer satisfaction and profit?

3 THE CUSTOMER INFORMATION SYSTEM

This chapter provides an overview of the main components of the customer information system. Much customer information arises from feedback from equipment servicing activities, but increasingly suppliers are finding the need to do direct customer research. So this chapter provides a guide to the key issues and techniques involved in customer research.

COMPONENTS OF CUSTOMER INFORMATION SYSTEM

The main components of the customer information system are:

Internal reports, covering current equipment performance (reliability, parts usage, etc.), engineer and other service staff performance (e.g. hours, costs), other costs, parts and equipment inventories, cash flows, growth of base of equipment to be serviced, and accounts. Some of this information may come from other functions (e.g. sales and marketing, accounting, production)

Commercial intelligence system, by which everyday information is received about commercial developments, i.e. who (customers, distributors, competitors) is doing what in the market today and what are they planning to do. Sources include publications, conversations with suppliers, distributors, customers and competitors, feedback from the sales and service force, exhibitions, competitors' price lists and annual reports.

Customer research, by which information is systematically collected on particular topics. This may overlap with the intelligence system.

Analysis, by which information from these sources is built into a coherent picture. Analysis works by selecting material, interpreting it, building models to explain it, relating the explanations to policy decisions, evaluating options against the information, and ensuring that the conclusions are taken into account in decisions.

UNDERSTANDING THE CUSTOMER

To formulate service policy, we must understand customers in some depth, in particular their attitudes to service, when service is important in equipment acquisition or why different customers buy different levels of service. We must take into account the many determinants of customer behaviour, such as:

Economic: Purchasing power (which depends on income, assets, cash and finance costs or facilities), price (of product in question, substitute or complementary products) or use costs.

Influence: The most powerful influence may be reference groups, including peer groups (colleagues at work or in other establishments) and aspirational groups (other companies who are looked up to in some way - hence the common phenomenon of small businesses buying products and services which they regard as most suitable for larger companies).

Product / supplier experience: The repeat buyer often behaves very differently from the first time buyer. The repeat buyer who was satisfied with his last decision may go through a quicker decision cycle, and search for fewer alternatives. But if the repeat buyer's expectations were too high, the converse may be true.

Channel experience: A dealer's before and after-sale service may be good enough to create over-riding loyalty in choice of equipment and service.

Service mix: The products available, and how they are priced, promoted and distributed. Different customers are affected in different ways - some may be price sensitive, others sensitive to how service is 'packaged'.

Perceptions: Customer behaviour is founded on perceptions, not facts. What counts is perceived service and value, not any objective measure.

Innovativeness / risk taking: Customers may be innovative purchasers, followers, or laggards, risk accepters or avoiders, particularly with respect to new products (e.g. remote diagnostics), and between products and service (e.g. risk takers on equipment, but not on after-sales service)

INFORMATION FROM THE MARKETING FUNCTION

The demand for service stems from the demand for equipment, which in turn stems from demand for the services of that equipment, or 'demand for use'. The latter topic more properly belongs to the marketing function. However, the marketing function may 'skip' straight to the second stage (demand for equipment), since their profit comes principally from the supply of equipment. Customers need to carry out particular tasks. The equipment configuration (mix, durability, load capacity) to perform those tasks is devised and presented to the customer as a solution to his needs. Current totals and forecasts of the total amount of equipment to be serviced are normally passed to the service function, which is then left to try to understand those parameters of the use situation which determine service policy. The marketing function's understanding of the use situation can be used to improve service policy making. This applies for example when some equipment is used more heavily by particular customers, or when the level of service required from equipment affects the configuration of equipment. For example, a customer may require fail-safe or fall-back equipment.

This kind of information may not be passed from sales/marketing to service for the latter to formulate a service policy for the customer or type of equipment in question. This is the origin of some customer satisfaction problems. The result of this is that the service function may have to start from square one in obtaining information, rather than taking the situation at time of sale and seeing whether the use situation has changed since then.

Value of information from marketing

Information from marketing is valuable for two reasons. At the individual level, it affects the level of service that might be given to the individual customer, to keep his level of satisfaction high, and it determines the type of service contract that is likely to be saleable to him. At the aggregate level, this data determines the overall resourcing of the service function. Equipment which is in general being sold for 'non- critical' use demands less service resource than equipment which is in general sold for 'critical' use. This information is particularly important for companies breaking new ground, either with a product line whose service and/or use characteristics are significantly different from its existing products, or where marketing policy is taking existing products into markets where use characteristics will differ. The data also affects the kind of service contract (price, terms, guarantees, etc.) that should be offered in general, as well as other aspects of service marketing (e.g. how service is promoted). In other words, it represents a vital store of customer information.

So, the first input into determining the demand for service should be data arising from the sale situation about the demand for services that the equipment will provide. For equipment which is sold and serviced by the same company, this may mean using the salesman to report data to the service function, possibly at local level, as well as in a centralised way (for planning purposes). This does not mean turning the salesman into a market researcher for the service function. It does mean that critical data on the use situation should be provided in summary form to the service function. Where service is provided by another company in a non-competitive way (e.g. by a distributor), this may mean the centralisation of data and transfer in summary form at a higher level. The information listed below would normally be covered in selling and not require special sales research (particularly dangerous on questions of reliability or service - the last thing a salesman wants to mention when he is trying to close a sale).

Information obtainable from marketing function
- Whether other equipment is available to provide the service.
- Availability of outside services to perform some or all of tasks.
- Criticality of service to processes of department, site, company etc.
- Likely loading of the equipment (frequency of use, peaking, etc., at different times of day, week, year, etc.).

The buying centre
The salesman will be in contact with the "buying centre" (all those who influence the purchase of equipment). But the influence of those most affected by the level of service may not be great, so we must be careful about arguing from attitudes on service to likelihood of repurchase. But relevant data on the composition of the buying centre should be passed to the service function.

RESEARCHING THE CUSTOMER
Information obtained in the selling process may be an aging source. As the number of customers or quantity of equipment serviced by a company gets to the size where it is no longer able to make policy on an individual basis (the size is determined by the frequency of demand for service as well as by size of installed base), customer research may be required. Customer research is a focused approach to gathering information about any aspect of actual or potential customer behaviour. Primary research is research that obtains data directly from the respondent. Secondary research uses data which has already been obtained for some other purpose. This section outlines the main principles of service customer research.

When to use research
Customer research can be used in any of the following situations.
- Deciding the nature of the service problem.
- Selecting a problem for solution.

- Policy making to solve the selected problem.
- Implementing the solution.
- Modifying the solution after receipt of first results.
- Deciding which problems occur often enough for a more general policy to be adopted to solve them.

Before committing resources to research, these questions must be answered:
- Is the required information already available?
- Has all available information been analysed properly?
- Have the relationships been correctly specified and modelled?
- What extra information is necessary in order to make the decision?
- How is it going to be obtained and at what extra cost?
- How is the information going to be analysed, and by whom?
- How is any forecasting going to be done? What assumptions will be made about the future values of key independent variables and about any change in the nature of relationships established on the basis of historic data?

INFORMATION SOURCES

The main sources of information in customer research are:

Secondary sources - Internal or external information already possessed, perhaps gathered for some other purpose. This category includes information coming from the sales force, service force and distributors as part of the normal management of the service operation. Such information is often used not to solve the entire problem but to aid modelling and design.

Respondents - Typically via questionnaire, though user groups may also fall into this category. The main questions here are:
- Are the respondents the right people to talk to? Should we be talking to buyers, users, influencers or operators?
- How are their responses to research related to their behaviour? Does the fact that they are being researched alter their response?

Observation - Where response to policy changes is observed and analysed. The key problem here is ensuring that other determinants of the outcome are properly understood and accounted for. Prototype or trial installations are a good example of this.

Simulation - Often useful in pilot stages of research, but rarely adequate as a firm basis for decision.

MAIN ELEMENTS OF RESEARCH

The four major stages of primary customer research are:

- Research design (including sample design and questionnaire design).
- Fieldwork.
- Data analysis.
- Interpretation of results.

Situation modelling

Prior to initiating research, it is important to determine how the results will be used. Customer research may aim to produce straight quantification e.g. how many customers or potential customers need a particular level of service. At its most useful, research aims to find causes or connections e.g. the effect on customer satisfaction of prioritising calls. This requires a model of the process or situation under investigation, or 'situation modelling'. The aim is to draw a hypothetical picture, showing broadly what is thought to be happening, and why (e.g. how customers behave when equipment fails, how they decide which service contract to buy). This picture is used to generate hypotheses about the situation. These hypotheses determine what needs to be researched. The less clearly defined the picture, the more information will need to be gathered 'just in case'.

Business modelling

The second type of modelling needed is 'business modelling', the modelling of the decisions for which the research is needed. It covers policy options, likely costs and benefits of particular decisions, and so forth. It covers all the topics listed in Figure 1.3 in Chapter 1. It answers the question 'what would we do if we had the information, and what might be the result?' For example, if we are investigating the effects of prioritising calls, we should have a reasonably clear idea of how we would implement the prioritisation.

Situation and business modelling play a prime part in research design. They help identify the variables to be included in the research, the required size and choice of sample, sources of information, mode of interviewing, and the analyses carried out on the information.

RESEARCH DESIGN

Work carried out prior to specification of the research design may involve:
- Exploratory studies (e.g. group discussions among users, operators).
- Searches of secondary sources.
- Consultation of experts or managers involved in the situation.
- Examination of case histories of similar situations.

Design activity focuses on deciding:
- Sources of information.
- Number of respondents.
- Method of choice of respondents.
- How respondents are to be accessed.
- How information will be obtained from them.
- How it will be prepared for analysis.

INTERVIEW METHODS

The best known form of gathering data from respondents is interviewing, the simplest form of which is the direct structured questionnaire, where all the questions are specified beforehand. Other forms include:
- Direct unstructured questioning (the interviewer is told no more than the general sort of information required), often used in exploratory studies (e.g. to establish the general parameters of customer needs).
- Indirect interviewing (where the respondent is effectively induced to project feelings, through word association, description of pictures, or sentence completion e.g. describing a situation of equipment failure).
- Focus group interviews (particularly useful at the design stage, especially to understand the language that respondents use).
- Third person techniques (respondents are asked what a third person thinks, etc.).

Information is obtained face-to-face, or by telephone or mail, with lower quality or probability of response compensated for by lower cost. Variations include warranty card returns and observation of customer behaviour.

Interview design

This relates to the questionnaire or interview's structure, length, question form and degree of formality of a questionnaire. The main approaches are:
Fully structured: The exact form and content of the interview is fixed.

Semi-structured: Some questions are very specific, while others allow less specific answers (i.e. a mixture of closed and open-ended questions).

Totally unstructured: The interviewer introduces the subject and allows the respondent to enlarge on it as he wishes (often used in qualitative research).

Prompts: Typically used in testing awareness. These can introduce bias, by creating awareness during the course of an interview. Even listing of suppliers in alphabetical order may create bias (order should be rotated).

For a questionnaire to work, the respondent must be able to understand every question and be able and willing to provide the information. A good questionnaire will have a logical sequence to it, and provide specific answers which can be easily and accurately recorded. The language it uses must be completely transparent to the respondent, and be very concise. It should not ask for opinions on third parties (hearsay), unless there is no option (e.g. 'Is your manager satisfied with the service on your equipment?'). Questions that are hypothetical or beg a response bring unreliable results. Long interviews must maintain the respondent's interest. 'Funnelling' (starting with simple, general, low-risk questions and slowly focusing on the prime theme) is useful if there is a risk of respondent sensitivity.

To ask if someone is a loyal customer is pointless. It is better to ask whether and why a customer is dissatisfied or has considered changing service supplier. Asking whether the customer would change supplier is a hypothetical question, which may produce an unreliable response. Asking directly about operator-induced failures is risky, as this tends to be understated.

Scaling

Scaled responses are an important component of most customer research. Methods used to elicit scaled response include the Likert scale, where a respondent is asked to say what his attitude is to a particular statement, on a 5 point scale from 'strongly agree' to 'strongly disagree'. In Guttmans scales, the scaling is built into the attitude statements i.e. the respondent is asked to say with which of a number of statements he or she agrees. Semantic differential scaling consists of asking the respondent to rate something on a number of different scales (e.g. simple to use to complicated to use, good value to bad value). The problem with this approach is that many of the words used are 'value-laden'. It may be difficult to find out what a respondent who rates something as bad value for money would regard as good value for money. However, this approach is valuable in identifying questions related to image (of self, of product, of company). For example, we might want to discover whether customers rate our service as good value for money. We could use:

The Likert approach:

It is good value for money

Strongly agree 5 Agree 4 Uncertain 3 Disagree 2 Strongly disagree 1

The Guttmans approach

It is very good value for money 5
It is good value for money   4
etc.

The semantic differential approach

The service is: Very good value.................................Very bad value

Over-sophisticated scaling techniques can obscure what might be quite a simple picture, e.g. by researching more dimensions of service than a customer really considers. Initial small group work is vital to establish which dimensions really are important to the customer. In general, scaling should be kept simple, without labels (e.g. bad, good, very good) whose meaning is unclear, and without long batteries of scales or rankings (which degrade the response). It is crucial to find some way to correlate scaling or ranking with behaviour. Some companies, embarking for the first time on customer research, produce immense research studies based upon extensive questionnaires. The quality of response is dubious, and the correlation with behaviour unknown.

FIELDWORK

The ideal method of fieldwork is the in-home or in-office face-to-face interview, but telephone and mail are commonly used. Telephone interviews are biased in favour of those who have telephones or those who happen to be at home or in the office at the time, if quota sampling is used (unless calling back is strictly adhered to). Mail surveys also suffer non-response bias unless non-respondents are followed up. Mail response may be increased by personalising the questionnaire, using stamps rather than business reply envelopes, and enclosing small gifts.

Most fieldwork is contracted to specialist researchers, who have staffs of interviewers (full and part time) backed up by field supervisors who call back to respondents to ensure that interviews are correctly carried out (or carried out at all!). Success in fieldwork depends partly on questionnaire quality, which depends partly on whether it has been piloted, to test for ease of administering, transparency of language, and so on.

New technology is beginning to have an effect on fieldwork. The traditional method of writing down responses is being replaced by direct terminal entry for telephone questionnaires. Portable terminals are making this viable for face-to-face work. Such methods avoid the necessity of a separate keying-in operation, while the software can be designed to prevent inconsistent answers and to steer the interviewer through a complex route in the questionnaire.

Because of difficulty in carrying out fieldwork, panels of customers may be used. Panels are composed of customers who agree (usually for a small reward) to submit regular reports (or to be interviewed regularly).

Companies undertaking customer research for the first time may insist on too rapid and comprehensive research, which can result in dubious results because of the demands that it imposes on fieldwork. Customer research is an investment, not just an ad hoc way of getting information, and should be well integrated with other parts of the customer information system. This will produce better, cheaper results in the long term.

COMMISSIONING RESEARCH

Once the nature of the required customer research is decided, a key question is whether to design and/or execute the research in-house or not. Most service operations, especially smaller ones, do not have the manpower or budgets to carry out surveys, so multi-client surveys may be used to spread the costs over several companies. Such surveys are good at giving the general picture (whether your customers rate your service well), but not good for fine detail. They are also liable to misinterpretation. If company X's customers rate some aspect of service higher than company Y's, does this mean that service is marketed well by company X, or that its service is better? What about customers with equipment from both X and Y? For these reasons, larger companies usually prefer to run their own surveys, to get the accuracy they require. If the survey is run on your own customers, it is possible to relate results to service records. Disparities usually emerge here, so do you trust the service records or what the users say (e.g. concerning response time)? These problems can be partly overcome by relating research to specific events rather than asking customers for generalised perceptions and requirements.

Companies embarking on their first service market research are advised to use experts. In-house market researchers understand the business better, so you will not be paying someone to learn, but they may be a little inward-looking, so it is advisable to use out-house researchers or agencies sometimes, to check the perspective of the research. These are expensive, so should be used only when there is clear benefit.

ANALYSIS AND INTERPRETATION

Analysis aims to clarify the findings of research, test their significance, and identify relationships between different findings. Interpretation relates to basing of policy conclusions on research. Much analysis is computerised. The data is collated, and typically arranged in tabular form, with columns and rows defined by 'breaks' which are thought to be particularly meaningful, or some other form (e.g. graphical). The more quantitative the questionnaire, the easier the analysis. Tests of significance have to be applied to check whether the variation between different cells in tables is significant, given the sample size. However, these tests cannot be applied to quota sampling, which break all the laws of random sampling on which significance tests are based.

Interpretation is the first step towards policy making. If the research was well specified, we should have been aiming to confirm or reject certain hypotheses about customer behaviour, and our research should have been structured to yield the result. Is satisfaction with our service rising or falling? Are we getting increased sales because of our service reputation? What are the critical signs of a highly dissatisfied customer, and how can we identify him as early as possible?

Despite the wealth of techniques available for interpreting data, the dominant modes of analysis are tabulation or comparison of crude averages, with much effort going into specifying tables, and little into discovering significant relationships. This may reflect inherent distrust of managers for statistics and desire to see the 'real' data (i.e the crude or weighted numbers). Multivariate statistical techniques have a hard fight for acceptance in some companies. Notwithstanding this, it is important to get some understanding of the structure of the data and relationships involved (e.g. are relationships linear, which variables are likely to be interrelated, and why).

SOURCES OF ERROR

The principal sources of error in research are:

Experimental error - Caused by:

- Not including relevant respondents in the base to be sampled from.
- Sampling non-randomly.
- Not allowing for the effects of bias in non-response.

Response error - When information collected is incorrect, or inaccurate. This is often caused by bad questionnaire design, including:

- Ambiguous questions.
- Vague or too broad specification of responses.
- Too lengthy questionnaires involving time costs for respondents.
- Questions involving respondent status or invasion of privacy.
- Leading questions.
- Questions assuming a level of respondent knowledge, understanding, commitment or motivation not actually present (a particular risk when there is a clear separation between users, purchasers and operators).
- Causing respondents to avoid perceived conflict with interviewer.
- Investigator unwillingness or inadequate reward.

A SAMPLE QUESTIONNAIRE STRUCTURE

There is no ideal questionnaire for customer research. Here, we outline a structure, including the main topics to be researched and the form questions might take. It is a menu, from which individual components can be chosen.

Introductory block - site and equipment identification

This is a set of questions which identify the main parameters of the equipment installed and the nature of their use. This is important, since even if the research is confined to a company's existing user base, there may be errors in the company's data base. In certain cases, the company may wish to concentrate on equipment of a certain vintage (e.g. last equipment acquired, equipment more than two years old). Questions here might refer to:

- The number and type of equipment in the site, department etc. (own, competitive, substitutional).
- Identification of other sites or departments in which equipment is used.

- Date of acquisition.
- Equipment recently disposed of.

Acquisition/disposal block

Different reasons tend to apply to different types, makes and models of equipment. We may need to know whether the equipment is for a new use, replacement or additional equipment. Given the many reasons why equipment may be acquired or disposed of, it is sensible to try to get respondents to prioritise their reasons, but we must be wary of respondent's tendency to post-rationalise. Questions may refer to:

Product / sales reasons

- Competitive/own marketing (equipment change suggested).
- Salesmen's attitude.
- Awareness of other makes and familiarity with them.
- Recommendation from other users (in/out-house).
- Purchase arrangements (contract, lease, etc.).
- Price.
- Features/performance.
- Perceived technology level of equipment.
- Supplier strengths/weaknesses.
- Selection process (how many other makes of equipment considered, evaluated, and in what detail, who involved).
- Demand for equipment capacity (rising/falling, new/discontinued use).
- Involvement of the respondent in the decision.

Service / use situation reasons

- Reliability (overall, trends) - uptime, call frequency.
- Service personnel - manner, skills.
- Degree of dedication of service staff to particular customer.
- Uptime or response time.
- Whether service by manufacturer or dealer.
- Call/downtime frequency.
- Length/frequency of parts wait.
- Existence or quality of preventative maintenance.
- Remote diagnostic/service facilities.
- Availability of help line or other means of avoiding calls.
- Availability of replacement equipment.
- Recurrence of particular faults.

- Service contract terms (flexibility, variety, length, etc.).
- Other aspects of relationship with supplier.
- Cost of operation.
- Availability and cost of supplies/ancillary equipment.
- Noise levels.
- Need for operator attendance.
- User friendliness.
- Ease of self-maintainability.
- Frequency/quality of machine modifications.
- Quality/coverage of operator training.
- Service billing and payment administrative arrangements.
- Availability/quality of third party service.

Whatever the reasons for acquisition or disposal suggested by the customer, remember that these are all *perceptions,* which may result from extensive post-rationalisation on his or her part. These perceptions are the 'facts' of the market place, but it is important not to argue directly from stated perceptions to the need to change policy. A stated dissatisfaction with level of service as a reason for disposing of equipment does not imply that the level of service should be improved. The existing level of service may be presented in a more positive light. A respondent may state that level of service was critical in acquiring or disposing, but never have evaluated (at all or in any depth) the service offered by competitors. This kind of data may need corroboration by sales staff.

Use pattern block

These questions seek to establish how the equipment is used. Since the demand for service depends upon use patterns, it is usually important to trace use patterns to individual equipment. It may be important to distinguish users, buyers and operators, since they may have very different requirements and different influences on future service and equipment purchases. This block of questions may also be applied to equipment disposed of. Questions may cover:

- Use patterns (type of work, volume, frequency, criticality, dependence).
- Identification of users (dedicated, casual, etc.).
- Responsibility for operation.

Perception of service block

This block is the core of most service research. It can usually be broken down into two major aspects, relating to perception of service delivered, and tolerance levels (e.g. best service required, worst service tolerated). In a very detailed questionnaire, it is easy to lose the wood for the trees. For this reason, it is usually wise to ask one or two very general questions relating to overall level of satisfaction with service and one or two of its major components (e.g. uptime, contracts), and major areas requiring improvement. These can usually be prioritised by the respondent. A more detailed level of research may even include research into the value of different levels. However, hypothetical valuation of benefits is one of the trickiest areas of research. It may be more appropriate to test market service products.

In detail, this block usually requires resolving service into its many detailed components (as per service/use reasons above) and questioning the respondent about his level of satisfaction with them, his perception as to what he is receiving at the moment, whether it has changed, tolerance bands, and degree of interest in other ways of receiving service.

Customer care block

Customer care programmes are becoming increasingly popular. These programmes normally demand a wider, more superficial level of questioning. However, the block of questions used for such studies may be incorporated in a more in-depth study, to test how customer care relates to other aspects of service. Typically, a customer care study involves frequent resampling of respondents to track how their attitude to service is changing over time.

Customer care studies should normally cover all aspects of the customer interface, not just service. The customer may not distinguish too well between service and other aspects. The field engineering side of the company may draw false comfort from a study which shows satisfaction with engineers and dissatisfaction with sales and company administration. This may indicate either that engineers have an inherent advantage in gaining customers' respect (they are after all the instrument by which customers' problems are solved) or that they have been denigrating the company so as to make their own jobs easier. The same may apply to the sales side (salesmen or store staff). Since in many ways they are charged with delivering the image of the company, a poor company image associated with a positive sales image may be due to sales staff committing the same error.

The questions in customer care studies should relate to the key elements of the human interface with the customer, covering such items as:

- The professionalism of the staff involved (knowledge of subject, handling of situation).
- Rapidity of resolution of any problems.
- Keeping the customer informed.
- Ease of contact.
- Response to problems.
- Help with training.
- Help with advice.

CHECKLIST FOR CHAPTER 3

* Are we using all available sources of customer information to enable us to optimise service policy?
* Do we have data on the determinants of our customers' demand for service?
* Do we receive data from the marketing and sales function concerning customers' buying centre composition and behaviour, the equipment use situation and customers' service requirements?
* If we do customer research, do we formulate a clear model of the situation we are researching?
* Do we know what kind of decisions we expect to be affected by the results of the research?
* Do we make full use of exploratory research and small group discussions to establish the general nature of problems and the language that customers use to describe these problems?
* If we use a market research agency, do we put the research out to competitive quote?
* When we research perceptions and attitudes towards failure, do we do so close enough to a failure to ensure accuracy of recall?
* Do we try to correlate the results of research with behaviour (e.g. renewal or cancellation of contracts)?
* Does our research allow for the effect of use-situation on customers' views of service?
* Do we research our customers regularly enough to build a clear picture of trends in their satisfaction with service and their attitudes to and perceptions of different elements of the service we provide?
* Do we integrate our research data with feed-back from the service force (and where appropriate, the sales force)?
* In interpreting our research data, are we careful not to read into it our own preferences or wishes? Are we certain that ratings of customer satisfaction (and movements therein) are statistically significant?

4 DESIGN, MANUFACTURE AND RELIABILITY

The underlying reliability of equipment is an important component of customer service. Some problems of inherent unreliability can be overcome by a well managed customer service operation, but a supplier whose equipment is much less reliable than its competitors may find it difficult to maintain customer satisfaction. Even if he succeeds, the cost may be high, since the price he can charge for customer service may be dictated by average industry reliability, while his costs may be higher than the industry standard.

High reliability - a problem?
Equipment which is 100% reliable poses a problem, especially for companies with large service operations. If the customer never needs a call, what is to be done with the service force? The reliability of equipment is improving with the substitution of electronic for electromechanical devices. This has also reduced the cost of most equipment. These trends will not necessarily reduce the cost of service visits or the frequency of servicing. The reduced cost of components is often exploited by increased device complexity (leading to increased performance). In some cases, additional facilities are offered locally where previously they were offered centrally (e.g. printing, for computers). On-site time may be reduced, but the cost of engineer travel and parts may increase, particularly with increasing use of module replacement. The future field service operation may have to make fewer visits, and be more effective in ensuring that it retains product profitability. Alternative repair methods may have to be used instead of the travelling technical expert.

PRODUCT RANGE
Design policy has a major effect on field service organisation. If equipment designs are similar, engineers should be able to deal with all technical service requests (or at worst specialise in one aspect of repair of all machines). The more complex and less uniform the product range, the more likely that service engineers will need to specialise by product.

New products

The central problem for designers is integrating new products into the range. Production and service costs are minimised by having a narrow range of products based on the same series of compatible modules, with new products being introduced by evolution, modules for the new equipment fitting the old, and old parts being upgradable to suit the new models. However, these requirements may conflict with the marketing need for completely new and radically different products. The more a product is seen to be different from the previous range the better. New technology is an advantage.

Revolutionary and evolutionary approaches

There are two main approaches to design, evolutionary and revolutionary. The evolutionary approach is strategically feasible if the company has a dominant market position (allowing it to overcome any possible marketing disadvantages of not being in the forefront) or if technology is evolving fairly slowly. In more competitive markets, or where technology is advancing more rapidly, a company may have little choice but to adopt the revolutionary approach, and wipe the slate clean for every new product.

In the evolutionary approach, technical goals of design teams are dictated by the needs of production and after-sales service (e.g. use of specific parts). The service operation benefits in terms of manpower utilisation, spares, and training time. In the revolutionary approach, designers may have freer scope, development is faster, and more flair applied. Design takes quantum leaps. This approach will not affect service and production costs too adversely if product planning focuses on product ranges rather than individual products. This demands a more comprehensive approach to the market place, but can yield big dividends. Maximal utilisation of standard parts from outside suppliers and designing to take advantage of the latest automated manufacturing equipment may make the revolutionary approach cheaper.

The modular approach

A compromise between evolutionary and revolutionary approaches is the modular approach, where equipment is designed as a collection of modules made by different suppliers (who may or may not include the principal manufacturer or assembler). Some modules may be used in several manufacturers' equipment. The technology of the finished machine may vary according to the particular modules used at the time of design or manufacture. Unless module suppliers themselves follow a policy of compatibility, it may be difficult for the main supplier to achieve a reasonable level of product compatibility.

Reducing diversity

Where a company's product range is diverse, engineers require different spares kits for each product (or product-specialised engineers require different kits). The service operation is then loaded with a wide range of slow moving stock. In companies which reduce their product range, engineer utilisation and spares availability increase, spares inventories decrease in value and engineer on-site time is reduced. Savings are also made in less obvious areas such as supercession planning and component obsolescence.

PRODUCT LIFE

Physical product life has an important effect on service costs. Physical life of equipment may be much longer than market life. Technical progress may mean that customers benefit from frequent equipment change, with the limiting factor being the customer's willingness to keep paying for new equipment and his ability to optimise the use of it. There may be a minimum natural life of equipment, particularly if it is the kind of equipment which forms part of a wider customer-based technical and human system (e.g. production machinery, office systems). This life can be divided into a number of phases, as follows:

- Installation of equipment and integration into customer's system.
- Settle-down period.
- Up-dating period.
- End of life.

Installation and integration

Installation and integration of the equipment into the customer's operating practices takes a while. In this period the machine is being matched to the customer's requirements. Unless it does not do the work required, changes made at this stage are generally additions or modifications. There may be an inflated number of breakdown calls, due to operator error.

Settle-down period

It may take some time for the customer's operators to become fully competent in using the equipment and for the customer to make full use of its potential. This period is relatively stable as far as the service engineer is concerned, though the causes of breakdown may change as the equipment gets older.

Up-dating period

The customer may become aware of the shortcomings of his equipment relative to more recent equivalents. If a modification is available to keep the equipment up-to-date, the engineer can continue to use his detailed product knowledge for existing modules and only have to learn about new ones, while the bulk of his spares kit will be applicable to the new modules. Commercial life can be extended by modular design if the original product architecture permits.

End of life

End of life occurs when customers realise that changing is better than up-dating the equipment. Customer equipment life is falling for many products. Minimum life depends partly upon the cost and complexity of equipment, since:

- High cost slows down the financial cycle for replacements.
- Complex equipment has longer learning times and may cost more.

Simpler, cheaper equipment may have a shorter minimum life. More complex, expensive equipment will have longer replacement cycles. Given improving reliability, engineers may not be able to get to know equipment well because the mean time between failure is long relative to commercial life. Suppliers should re-examine engineer training, call organisation and spares support levels in the light of this. Field engineering organisations will need to work more closely with design teams to ensure that launching and removal of models from the market takes place smoothly.

IMPROVED RELIABILITY

The electronic revolution led to increased reliability for given performance, coupled with increased performance for a given unit of equipment, with the net result being a more complex piece of equipment, sometimes more, sometimes less reliable than the process or equipment which it replaced. In some sectors the increase in reliability for given performance has so far outpaced the rising performance per unit as to produce a substantial increase in unit reliability. This means that there is less need for service engineers. However, in some cases wider market diffusion of the equipment will compensate for this.

Less consistent repair patterns
Higher reliability means less consistent repair patterns and possibly absence of enough data to establish a failure pattern or decide a spares policy. For large, complex but reliable equipment sold in small numbers, by the time a pattern emerges, the model may be greatly modifed or even changed completely.

Effect on engineers
If engineers specialise in particular products, improved reliability may mean:
- Increased engineer travel, or
- A wider range of equipment to service

The engineer of the future may have to travel further and know how to repair a larger variety of equipment than his predecessors.

DESIGN AND SERVICEABILITY
Technology and design have caused service to move through these stages:
- Skill and information-intensive.
- Module replacement/discrete component repair.
- Box changing.

Skill/information intensive phase
Originally, when the engineer made a service call, he was armed with a wealth of components and technical information, and a high level of skill, although these were not always needed. The engineer might spend a few hours executing a complicated repair. The equipment may have been relatively large, but the complexity and variety of operations (particularly for individual sub-elements of the equipment) was less. The cost of individual parts was usually small. The engineer could carry a wide range of parts, but the cost of his kit was low. This type of operation did not require tight control over spares supply.

Module replacement/discrete component repair
As technology advances, using engineers to identify a fault and rectify it by component replacement becomes less appropriate. With printed circuit boards (PCBs), on-site repair has become risky. Since the amount of circuitry on a PCB has increased as the size of components has fallen, there is now real danger of

damaging an expensive PCB by the application of fingers, soldering iron, or screwdriver in the wrong place. Board-swapping allows repairs to be made under controlled conditions at a repair centre with good test and repair equipment available. Other components, typically electro-mechanical ones, can still be repaired, though even here, the economics of replacement have been made more favourable as mass production has reduced costs.

Up to this stage, design focused mainly on functional or production issues (how to get a component to perform a certain operation, how to produce it cheaply). Companies struggled to achieve more with smaller, lower cost units. Gradually this drive led to diminishing returns. Profits from equipment were squeezed and the cost of service became an important issue. Design started to take into account the cost of service and the modular concept was developed.

Supplier marketing strategies may accelerate the move towards modular design. In computers, market specialisation led to the appearance of systems integrators and smaller manufacturers, dependent on the supply of modules to configure systems highly suited to the needs of their chosen market customers. In the extreme, modules may not be extensively tested together except on the customer's site. The picture of the customer taking delivery of many boxes from all over the world is all too familiar.

Repair methods

Repair methods have followed manufacturing and assembly philosophy. Module repair of components has led to a different type of service. The engineer calls, identifies the faulty module and replaces it. The skill required is less. The customer benefits via rapid and more effective repair, but may feel that the service cost is not justified by on-site time.

The design and use of larger PCBs has exacerbated the problem of spares cost. Where there were 3 or 4 smaller PCBs to do a job, there is now one expensive one. This has raised the cost of service in terms of stockholding, even if there are manufacturing and design advantages. PCBs are so expensive that they have to be repaired rather than replaced. This has led to a situation in some companies where the cost of stockholding is not seen as important, or at least these PCBs are considered exempt from normal stockholding rules. After all, it is argued, if the item is constantly being repaired then it never loses value. This philosophy leads to a lack of tight inventory management which lengthens repair cycle time and sucks in extra purchases.

Box changing

This concept is becoming increasingly fashionable. It suits the type of equipment provided by many companies. The cost of spares is higher, but very high value items are not provided for all engineers. If replacement units are held centrally, this increases the cost of engineer travel to collect them. Obviously, this philosophy can only apply to relatively portable items.

LIFE TIME COSTS

Cost of repair varies through a product's life. For each component there is a specific mode of breakdown. Electronic components usually fail randomly. There is an equal chance that an item will break down at any time during its life. The failure rate of mechanical components tends to increase exponentially as they approach their designed life. Costs are also incurred by breakdown caused by careless installation, inexpert initial use by the customer, and engineers trying to repair new equipment when they are unfamiliar with its design or breakdown pattern. Equipment failure rates are therefore usually high at the start, then decrease gradually, and rise when wear takes over. The failure rate does not decrease again as components are replaced because successive types of components start to fail. For most equipment the cost of materials required for a repair is similar throughout the life of the product, so the cost of service follows the same trend as the failure curve (See Figure 4.1).

End of life parts costs

When a product is at the end of its life, parts costs may increase. A lower installed base may mean that the demand for most of its parts is small. Some parts may have been standard components when the machine was designed, but are now obsolete. There may be problems in finding new sources, obtaining parts, or having them manufactured. It may take extra time to obtain these parts, so stock holding may need to be higher to achieve service targets. There is also a risk that parts will have to be written off because they are never used. The parts cost allowance for servicing obsolescent equipment should be high enough to take into account the increased cost and higher write-off rates.

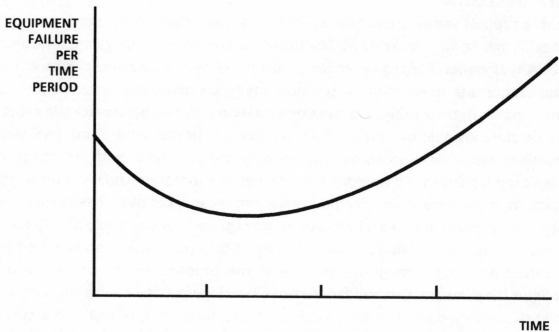

Figure 4.1 Failure Rate

For other components, there may be a cost saving at the end of product life because parts can be stripped from other equipment. This is useful for random failure items, as their reliability is not impared by previous usage. For wear items, the parts on scrap machines are likely to be worn. These may last a short time and lead to an increasing number of calls and high engineer costs. Any new parts in scrap equipment should be stored for future use. The cost of reclaimed parts is a proportion of the cost or allowance on the old equipment (depending on whether cannibalised machines have any hope of re-installation, and on the benefits to the company of re-installation), plus any cost of removing, refurbishing and transporting them. Where many items of equipment are being returned from the field, most demands can be satisfied from existing equipment and the cost of service may be reduced for a while.

RELIABILITY AND SERVICE PRICING

Products vary in their length of life and their peak unreliability (at beginning and end of life) relative to mature reliability. The best equipment is clearly characterised by a long, low flat section of the reliability curve, and small peaks at either end. If the customer is paying for the repairs on a time and materials basis then his costs vary with failure rate. Full service contracts based on a sum fixed in advance should take into account the expected lifetime of the equipment, its reliability and service cost profile.

If a supplier fixes the price of a service contract in real terms for the life of the product, then he must allow for variations in service costs by averaging costs out over the expected product life. A more subtle approach is to take into account the cash flow effect of profit variations over product life (profit will be low or negative at first, then higher, finally lower or negative). Such approaches may be vulnerable to competitors supplying equipment of identical reliability, who offer service contracts based upon costs up to but not including the period near end of life, and then charge a premium for this period. The market may well sustain this premium, since customers with products near end of life may have written off the equipment cost. However, there will still be a risk of third party maintenance suppliers attempting to sell service contracts based on maturity-only failure rates, with the same end of life pricing for end of life failure rates.

Competitors may see such a life-time average cost pricing structure as creating a market opportunity, and proceed to design products which are cheaper to produce, have shorter lives, and a short period of high, end-of-life service costs. This is a clear demonstration of the risks of cost-plus pricing. Even though in the last analysis we may need to use some version of cost plus pricing, we should not ignore the opportunities and risks which result from the customer's perception of what constitutes a reasonable service pricing policy.

A simple annual contract gives the equipment supplier the option to change the price each year and optimise his profits. But too much variation in contract prices may cause problems. Customers may find it difficult to accept that what is apparently the same contract varies in price. They are unlikely to have very accurate perceptions of reliability, or to be sympathetic to end of life parts problems. Such contracts can be marketed successfully, provided steps are taken to communicate the basis of pricing. Suppliers are normally unwilling to charge customers with old equipment (who are likely to be buying new soon) the full cost of their service. This also applies to time and materials service, though such non-contractual customers are often less firmly enmeshed in the supplier's marketing net than contractual customers, so the likelihood of repurchase from the supplier may be lower. Usually companies aim for a constant service price and so try to avoid these changes. Marketing of customer service should aim to reduce the sensitivity of customers to service contract prices. In addition, closer co-ordination between sales and service operations is likely to reduce any friction caused by end of life service pricing, and maximise opportunity for repeat sales.

END OF LIFE POLICIES
Companies which rent equipment or have strong market control (i.e. their customers accept any reasonable suggestion about end of life products) may be able to remove the oldest equipment from the field so as to reduce the service costs. For rental equipment, this may not be the least cost solution because such equipment is likely to be fully depreciated, but can have advantages from the marketing point of view (customers should be more satisfied). Many companies experience difficulty in controlling the age population for equipment. This fluctuates due to sales peaks as new models come out and roughs as model ranges age. If service costs are very high, then phasing of sales to reduce service costs may be appropriate. This may avoid the number of service calls being high in some years and low in others. As companies like to retain their engineer expertise this can result in poor engineer utilisation. Parts inventories may also

be difficult to manage. So one element of commercial strategy should be target lifetimes for equipment based on the technical advantages of the new products and the relative cost of maintaining the machines, taking into account the competitive position.

AUTOMATIC DIAGNOSTICS

The impact of automatic diagnostics is just beginning to be felt in many sectors. The equipment technology is widely available. Lower microprocessor costs have allowed suppliers to build them in to monitor various functions (electronic or electro-mechanical), transmit error messages, switch-in reserve circuits, and so on. Fault tolerant equipment owes its existence to enhanced internal diagnostic routines. In computing, fault tolerance may take the form of parallel processing and deletion of a processing element if it shows signs of a fault, or by automatic switching in of stand-by elements when the main element fails. However, further changes in service systems (computer, communications and human) are often required before diagnostic technology can be exploited to the full.

Initially, diagnostics were used to identify the location (module or individual part) of a fault, enabling a less skilled engineer to change the affected part. Three main approaches to the use of diagnostics exist:

Remote: test routines may be run remotely, and faults automatically notified to the service company.

Integral: requiring the customer or the engineer to report the fault.

Internal: the equipment applies the diagnostics and solves the problem itself.

Remote diagnostics

Much equipment can be designed to work with one or the other approach. If a machine has a communications facility, then many test routines that can be run on site can be run remotely, either on a health check basis, to pick up faults (or signs of imminent faults) before the customer notices, or when failure has occurred. For fault tolerant equipment, the self-testing routines are run to identify failed parts. Manufacturers claim that with remote diagnosis, maintenance costs (and charges?) can be reduced. Engineers with special skills, less common spare parts, and so forth, can be allocated better. Non-critical failures can be detected before they become critical, and be built into a preventive maintenance calling system. Equally important, remote diagnosis may establish that there is not actually a fault of the kind described by the operator, enabling the problem to be solved without a call at all. Some suppliers have claimed maintenance cost savings of up to 20%. To date, advanced remote diagnostics tend to be used for high-cost large equipment, particularly by suppliers with a widely dispersed installed base.

Customer uncertainty

One problem of remote diagnosis for computers is fear that suppliers might interfere with the customer's system, obtaining confidential information, preventing it working at crucial times, or modifying software without notice.

Opportunities in computing products

The major area of opportunity for remote diagnosis in computers is the more expensive peripherals (high capacity storage, advanced printers), where there is still a major mechanical element and where failure frequency is much higher. Leading suppliers are already introducing remote diagnostics to these products. However, many problems on such equipment have to be resolved by an engineer's call, since a mechanical adjustment or replacement will be required. The technology that is developed here can be used to increase customer self-service, combined with higher on-site parts holding.

Design implications

More advanced diagnostics allow fault identification at device level. If this is available, why remove, replace, repair and stock modules, when the problem can be solved by changing a single component. This means designing equipment that is repairable by less skilled staff (without risk) by device replacement. This may lead to demountable items, rather than to complex modules, harder to repair and increasingly expensive. If such trends appear, the engineer will be carrying a wide range of low value components in his kit again. This may then be used on a far wider range of products than modules can be.

Less system failures

In computers, increased use of all kinds of diagnostics, combined with distributed processing and networking, is gradually eliminating 'system' failure. Failure may be noticed only by slower processing, or the failure of a few terminals, but most of the system will keep working. For larger systems, the skills required to diagnose remotely may need to be concentrated in centres covering whole countries, continents or even the world. These centres usually work well defined escalation procedures.

Engineer implications

Faced with reduction in required skill levels through board and module swapping, engineers may see a further reduction in use of their skills, due to remote diagnosis. Disposability, module swapping and portability may turn the skilled service engineer into a serviceman-driver, similar to a domestic appliance engineer. Alternatively, there will be no breakdown calls. The equipment supplier will receive failure messages, then run remote diagnostic routines, and schedule calls for parts replacement. The customer will not have to wait for a repair before continuing work. He may never notice the failure. The need for rapid response is reduced and the engineer can repair at his convenience (or that of his customer). The speed of response required will depend upon the chance of a duplicate system failing before the call. It may be more economic to provide customers with a stock of those items where failures are noticeable, than to support a particular response time. Under this scenario, future engineers may have longer travel distances, lower skills, more types of equipment to service, calls planned well ahead, and responsibility for adjustment and parts or module replacement only. Skilled technical staff may still be needed to deal with difficult problems the engineer cannot solve.

Effect on competition

The competitive structure of service markets may change, with a larger number of companies chasing a falling volume of business. Service margins would be cut. The survivors may end up running local repair centres serving a variety of suppliers, with the latter providing technical support for problem solving.

MINIMISING LIFE CYCLE COSTS

The separation of responsibility for design, production, financing, sale and maintenance of equipment can have serious consequences for the total life-time costs (to supplier and user) of an item of equipment over its life. Realisation of how great these costs can be has led to development of a number of concepts, in fields such as quality and asset management.

Definition of asset management

Asset management (AM) is defined as 'The application of management, financial, engineering and other practices to achieving economic total-life costs of the equipment'.

This does not refer to 'minimising' costs. There may be a trade-off between cost reduction and the investment necessary to realise it. It may be better to design products to be scrapped after a given period, beyond which there is no concern about costs (so long as the customer knows what that period is!). The discipline of AM is applied to specification and design for reliability of equipment, its production, installation, commissioning, maintenance, modification and replacement, and feedback of information on design, performance and costs. The AM perspective helps the supplier to understand and improve total user costs and benefits, thereby improving marketability of products, providing for better after-sales service at lower cost, and potentially improving profitability over the product life.

AM demands application of a broad range of disciplines. In many companies, AM standards are low, because interdependence between the areas for which the different disciplines are responsible is often ignored. Most equipment suppliers do not allocate the responsibility for cost of ownership to any one department. Cost of ownership normally emerges as a result of many separate design, production, service, financial and marketing decisions.

Key dimensions of asset management
Two key dimensions of AM are costs and the length of equipment life during which it yields benefits, to the user and the supplier. For the supplier's marketing purposes, it is the buyer's perception of AM factors and the buyer's actual (rather than optimum) way of dealing with them that are important.

Costs
These can be split into those incurred by the supplier and those incurred by the user. There is no fixed rule about who incurs which costs for a given item of equipment, as this is often subject to the particular contractual arrangements and use-situation relating to each item of equipment (e.g. the terms of sale and service. There are two cost categories, as follows:

Product or equipment inherent costs - those incurred in the process leading to the availability of the equipment to provide its service, including:
  - Research.
  - Design.
  - Development (including prototypes and feasibility studies).

72

- Testing.
- Production.
- Quality control.
- Inventory holding.
- Physical distribution.
- Installation (including site preparation).
- Purchase finance.
- Application feasibility studies (including those for particular users).

Use costs - those incurred once the equipment has started to provide its services. They include:
- Cost of associated inputs (direct, support, training).
- Insurance and other ownership costs.
- Maintenance costs.
- Downtime costs (e.g. lost output, replacement equipment).
- Replacement costs.
- Disposal costs.

Product life
This is defined as the period over which the user evaluates the costs and benefits of the product, or as the supplier's evaluation period. The two may not be identical. Both may be determined by accounting conventions, or by expected physical life of the product (e.g. until scrapping or replacement).

In this section AM is considered from the standpoint of the supplier. The user's approach is therefore examined from a marketing and service perspective. How he manages his assets affects which products he is more likely to buy, how much he will be prepared to pay, what he will use them for, and how he will demand service.

Cost of ownership can be defined to exclude costs of operation (e.g. power, supplies, supervision), but to include all costs of maintenance (i.e. of keeping the asset serviceable. However, costs of operation should be included if there is a trade-off between the two. Improved supervision of the use of an asset may lead to reduced maintenance costs.

COMMUNICATION IS CRUCIAL!

Many problems of AM can be traced to failures in communication between different departments. Communication is a crucial element in asset management. Here, are some examples of the kind of communication required.

Between production and design

The production function should provide guidelines to the design function to ensure that parts are designed to be manufacturable. The design function should give early indication to the manufacturing function of parts design, to provide the opportunity for feedback as to manufacturability. Parts which are more difficult to manufacture will not only cost more, but are likely to have higher defect rates, and possibly higher failure rates in operation.

Between after-sales service and production

The service function should provide data which allows the manufacturing function to identify where failure is due to manufacturing quality problems. It should also provide guidelines as to how products should be tested for robustness by simulating field conditions.

Between design and after-sales

The service function should provide data to help the design function to identify where failure is due to design, and guidelines to help them design products and parts which are easier to service and test, whether by the customer, field engineers or in the service centre.

Between after-sales or manufacturing and purchasing

The service and manufacturing functions should provide data enabling the purchasing function to identify where problems or failure are due to faulty bought-in materials or parts, and guidelines to help the purchasing function improve the quality of these parts. These guidelines should be passed on to suppliers to encourage them to improve the quality of their products.

Between marketing and other functions

The marketing function should indicate the estimated costs to the company (e.g. discounts given, investment in keeping customers or replacing lost customers), of reliability problems. They should also supply data indicating customer requirements as to reliability, and the opportunities for involving the customer in sustaining product reliability or in servicing the product.

Between finance and other functions

The finance function should provide estimates of the costs of producing or buying and holding spare parts inventory to cater for failures, and of other elements of service cost attributable to failure or inferior performance.

Between field service and finance

The service function should indicate what resources are required to maintain equipment in the field, under different reliability assumptions.

Between customer and supplier

Customers should indicate to suppliers the full cost of failures, enabling the supplier to work out the marketing advantages of improving reliability.

Asset management audits

These and other required information flows will only take place if management realises the importance of AM, puts in place the systems to ease the flow of the right information, and positively reinforces these flows. This may involve regular AM audits of particular products, programmes or departments, to check:
  - Whether the flows exist.
  - Whether they are of the required level of accuracy.
  - How frequently they take place.
  - How they are used to improve reliability.
  - What the incentives are for the information to be used.
  - Whether the authority structure allows it to be used.
  - Whether the appropriate consultations take place.
  - Whether the usefulness of the information is fed back to its providers.
  - What rewards exist for improving performance or life cycle costs.

The existence of such flows is no guarantee that the right decisions will be made. Unless there is a shared understanding of the importance of asset management in all its dimensions, formal information flows may not help much. This may be helped by ensuring that the staff concerned either have worked in other functions affected by AM, or kept fully informed of its total context, rather than just the individual aspects that concern them. So, design engineers need to understand product usage patterns and the problems faced by marketing or service staff in dealing with different kinds of usage problems.

RULES FOR IMPROVING ASSET MANAGEMENT
There are a number of rules which individual functions should follow. These are not hard and fast, but indicate how AM might be improved.

Rules for general management
- Understand the AM concept and ensure that decision, communication and financial processes required to improve it are in place.
- Ensure that AM criteria form part of product and investment appraisal.
- Ensure that all the communication required for improved AM takes place.
- Ensure (via training or other means) that all relevant staff in the company understand the concept.
- Provide incentives to all relevant staff and to customers (where appropriate) to suggest ways of improving life time costs.

Rules for designers
- Understand their role in improving life-cycle costs and ultimately marketability of the product.
- Always use cost of ownership as a critical design criterion, and take best competitive achievements (or outlooked achievements, where standards are improving rapidly) as a minimum target.
- State cost/reliability assumptions made in designing the product, and ask for these to be confirmed by purchasing, production, service, marketing and financial staff.
- Be involved in product planning decisions, to ensure that changes in performance specifications are not made without examination of all costs.
- Be involved in preparation of after-sales support systems, from field maintenance practices and documentation, to customer care programmes.
- Be involved in decisions concerning acquisition of manufacturing equipment which might affect product quality.
- Ensure that they receive appropriate information from other functions to enable them to understand life cycle costs of different designs.

Rules for service managers

- Understand that their role in the system is not one of fixing problems, but of providing the means for giving the customer better service by understanding how equipment is used in practice, how it fails in practice, and what can be done to improve reliability.
- Attempt as far as possible to develop systems which allow the establishment of life cycle costs for particular products.
- State major assumptions made concerning provision of service (costs, management structure, operating practices, reliability data provision, etc.), to ensure compatibility with asset management approach and availability of required data for other functions. This applies in particular to the decision whether to have preventive or failure-only based maintenance.
- Be involved in product planning decisions (for same reason as designers).
- Be involved in design process, to ensure design for maintainability and reliability, including ease of diagnosis, condition monitoring, introduction of remote diagnosis and remote repair facilities, etc.
- Be involved in analysis of users' trade-off (if any) between product cost and after-sales cost.
- Be involved in analysing company trade-off between product cost and after-sales cost, to ensure understanding of need for service efficiency.

Rules for purchasing managers

- Understand role in ensuring quality of all purchased materials.
- Have key responsibility for monitoring and improving quality of purchased materials, components or sub-assemblies.
- Ensure that suppliers are aware of the life cycle implications of improved reliability of goods supplied.
- State purchasing decision assumptions, in particular relating to initial/subsequent cost trade-off.
- Detail the life cycle costs of purchased inputs.
- Be involved in relevant parts of product planning and design process, to ensure that reliability aspects of purchased materials or components are taken into account, and to ensure that purchasing function understands which inputs are particularly sensitive on reliability.
- Liaise with production and quality control functions to ensure understanding of production-related aspects of reliability of inputs.

Rules for accountants
- Develop decision and monitoring systems which take into account life cycle costs (direct and indirect) of all decisions (in particular the trade-off between cheaper manufacture and higher use costs).
- Ensure that information to support these systems is supplied.
- Ensure that analyses based on life-cycle costings are effectively communicated to appropriate decision makers.

Rules for marketing management
- Understand use-situation of products supplied.
- Ensure that customers' needs for reliability and particular life cycle cost profiles are researched and understood.
- Establish whether customers have AM processes in place.
- If so, establish which are the key decision-making individuals or departments who understand and are responsible for the application of AM techniques.
- Establish particular customers' mode of approach to AM, in order to flex product/marketing mix appropriately.
- Ensure that customer needs are clearly communicated to product planners, designers and other key functions, in terms that are meaningful to them, and at appropriate decision times.
- Ensure that information on other solutions available to customers (e.g. competitive products), and on customers' trade-off between initial cost and life-cycle savings, is conveyed to relevant functions, to provide targets for life cycle costs of supplier's products.
- Understand the place of life-cycle reliability in the total product-price-support mix, in order to optimise relevant marketing mix decisions.
- Ensure that all the relevant after-sales support actions (from physical distribution, installation and commissioning, through manuals and customer training, to parts inventory and maintenance service) are implemented so as to minimise the impact of any after-sales problems.

LIFE CYCLE COST ACCOUNTING
Following AM principles may be difficult because of the frequent split of an asset's life cycle between manufacturer and user (perhaps complicated by use of third parties to sell and/or maintain). The manufacturer may be responsible for specification, design, manufacture and perhaps installation, while the user may

be responsible for installing, commissioning, operating and disposing of the asset, and possibly for maintenance.

Analysing true life cycle costs involves the following:
- Identifying design and manufacturing costs.
- Obtaining a reasonable estimate of the life of the asset, under different operating conditions, usage intensities, etc.
- Identifying installation, commissioning and run-up costs.
- Isolating individual causes of failure, and their frequency in different operating conditions.
- Estimating the failure rate and downtime over its life.
- Forecasting spares requirements and associated costs.
- Forecasting labour and other costs of maintenance.
- Forecasting likely modification requirements (whether for technical user need reasons)
- Identifying categories of user costs of downtime or sub-standard performance and forecasting them.
- Forecasting disposal value.

At the design stage, much of this data will be relatively crude, resulting from experience of maintaining similar equipment, or from bench testing under conditions which may not be the same as those under which the customer will use the equipment. Further, equipment which is radically different from previous equipment sold by the company may cause problems for service engineers, requiring a long learning time until adjustment. However, if conscious effort is made to improve the quality of information available at the design stage, then reasonable accuracy may be achieved.

QUALITY AND MAINTAINABILITY
'Quality is free', as the saying goes, meaning that improvement in quality yields its own rewards, by reducing wastage of materials, components, staff time and so on, increasing customer satisfaction, and bringing greater market success. For equipment which has to be serviced, the situation is slightly more complex. Equipment service (as opposed to customer service) can depend on lack of perfect quality. Improved quality results in a reduced demand for maintenance, which eventually (though not immediately) may cut the revenue and profit that can be earned from service. All the more necessary, therefore, for suppliers to

switch to a philosophy of customer service, managing the after-market in an integrated fashion, leveraging strength with the customer to sell products other than equipment service.

Once one company in a sector pursues quality, all must, for fear of being left behind. Those who are ahead on quality can charge the same price for service as the others, and get a higher margin, even if the price of service is falling. As field service is a key source of information needed to improve equipment quality, and since the service organisation can itself improve through adopting quality programmes, we review here in brief some of the major characteristics of the drive for quality.

Costs of inferior quality

The costs of lack of quality arise in three main areas, as follows:
- Appraisal costs.
- Failure costs.
- Prevention costs.

Appraisal costs are caused by the need to have mechanisms to identify quality problems. These include inspection and testing facilities, statistical quality control, process control and manufacturing surveillance.

Failure costs are borne directly by both supplier and customer, depending upon the contractual arrangement between them and on the wider consequences of failure. They include scrap (including total resources invested up to the time of scrappage), costs of rectification, re-inspection, trouble shooting to determine the causes of failure, warranty costs, and customer problem costs (e.g. resources wasted because of the failure of equipment).

Prevention costs are typically design, engineering, purchasing and manufacturing routines, planning processes, quality audits (internal and of suppliers), and developing and implementing of quality improvement programmes.

Origin of quality problems

Quality problems arise for various reasons, particularly failure to follow asset management principles. The reasons can be classified as follows:
- Ignorance of the nature of the problem - the company may in general be well managed, but has not applied its talents to this problem.

- Lack of integration in decisions - typically designing products without using criteria which relate to what happens to the product later on manufacture, packing, distribution, installation, use, modification, upgrading and service. This failure to integrate may be due to divisions of responsibility between different departments or professions.
- Lack of discipline in internal processes relating to any aspect of a product's history (e.g. failure to trace recurring field failure to a particular part). This is often related to failures in company reporting and control systems, slack specification or design procedures (leading to lack of comprehension and consequent error), or laxity in allowing continuous respecification of design goals.

Role of service in improving quality

Service has a key role to play in improving quality. Firstly, it can examine its own processes for defects of the above kind. Secondly, it can contribute to understanding the nature of the product quality problem by ensuring that the real costs of lack of quality after the product has left the factory are documented and communicated to design and manufacturing functions. This communication may be improved by inclusion of service experts in design and manufacturing teams. This information should include data on customer costs, which eventually affect the product's marketability.

Quality circles

Quality circles are not the only way to improve quality, but they can produce great improvement in work processes, improving quality and reducing costs. Some companies have applied the concept specifically to groups of field engineers, with good results, whether in terms of customer care, reduced service costs, or increased identification of sales opportunities. Quality circles provide a grass roots approach to quality improvement. Experience shows that, introduced carefully and run under appropriate guidance, with disciplined record-keeping and top management backing, they not only lead to quality improvements, but also raise levels of motivation in the work force.

Many companies have improved quality without using quality circles. If quality problems are company-wide, a comprehensive programme of identifying all major cost-wasters, establishing the costs of quality, ranking them in order of wastefulness, selecting and correcting the major wasters, may be appropriate.

SOFTWARE PRODUCTS: RELIABILITY AND MAINTENANCE

Software support is beginning to cause increasing concern to computer and software suppliers. Software maintenance may account for well over half the cost of a development project. This is serious, given that software maintenance is not well understood, and often delegated to junior programmers or staff who have not been accorded the status of designers or programmers. Better specification and design techniques are slowly leading to improved quality. The realisation that continuous revision of specifications during the course of development is one of the prime reasons for software unreliability may lead to improved management of software development.

Software design approaches

Crude bugs and errors are a falling proportion of software problems. Changing user requirements, leading to addition of modules, may be a greater cause of problems. For this reason, improved design processes, with "hooks" to attach extra modules, may help. However, modularity can be an expensive solution, causing longer design cycles and performance problems. Major improvements may come from improved user requirements analysis and software specification techniques. These will reduce later modifications or make them easier, by documenting the kind of changes that users might want, so that software developers can build the appropriate flexibility into design.

Prevention, not cure

As with hardware, the best solution is prevention, not cure. Development tools for increasing programming productivity are being used to reduce faults. These tools may focus on both design and testing. One computer supplier radically improved the quality of its software by applying these tools, together with rigorous quality control standards. This is a simple extension of hardware design philosophy (design for reliability and maintainability) into the area of software. That it has taken so long for such practices to emerge may be due to the low priority so far given to the problem. To date, the key concern may have been to get the software to the market at all. One problem may be that with software, the designers are also responsible for production, and the designers do not understand reliability and maintenance.

New software support companies

The difficulty some software suppliers have in dealing with maintenance has led to the emergence of specialist software support companies, similar in some respects to third party hardware service companies. The opportunity emerges when the equipment supplier cannot provide total cover, or where a customer has a lot of third party software. This business has to be priced very carefully. One approach used it to have a contract fee, plus extra payment for time. As insurance, the support company may carry out an audit beforehand, to identify inadequate documentation and other risks.

Separating maintenance and development

Just as hardware maintenance is separated from hardware design and production, some suppliers separate software maintenance from development, to create a clear methodology and management responsibility for handling maintenance. The knowledge built up by maintenance specialists can be transferred to development teams, perhaps by involving maintenance specialists at all stages of development. This ensures that the software is designed to include capacity for later robust modification. The reverse flow is also important, with development staff being transferred into the maintenance team. This reflects practice in hardware engineering, where design for manufacturability is helped by involving production specialists in design, while manufacturing processes may be improved by involvement of product design specialists.

Measuring software quality

Producing quality indices for hardware has not been difficult. Failures can be attributed to particular components, and field service operations may provide ample data to measure failure rates. Measurement is a first step to improvement. One obstacle to improved software quality and maintainability is the difficulty of producing a quantitative estimate of quality (and the associated measure - productivity). This is often left to intuition, but methods are now being evolved for measuring software quality. These tools will increase the ability to identify low quality software and likely problems of over- complexity, and eventually provide criteria for selection of design method. Such tools will help in ensuring that subsequent modifications observe standards, increasing maintainability and useful life of core software.

Initial work on software quality was carried out using communications and information theory to identify program complexity. Design theory has been adapted for use in this area. Good design may be seen as one where connections between different elements are minimised in number, as most problems occur with connections between elements or modules. Having a way of keeping track of all interconnections is a great advance, since subsequent modifications can take account of these interconnections more easily.

Certification schemes

One approach to increasing quality is via company or national certification schemes. The concern for quality has given rise to companies specialising in software validation. Certification is thought to be applicable to reliability, functionality, user friendliness, documentation and programming standards.

Structured programming

Structured programming is one way to increase software quality, but may result in higher prices, simply because of the greater development resource required. This assumes that reliability has no pay-off in the market through increased sales or faster launch, or later through reduced maintenance costs. The issue here may be over who pays maintenance costs. Structured programming produces consistency, but involves training and other initial costs. Some software producers may be able to adopt programming tools which are more specific to their specialism, allowing a better pay-back. However, in the end customer demand for reliability may force faster adoption of structured approaches.

Other approaches

These include:

Source control code systems (SCCS) store the original version of a software system, together with all subsequent changes. When a version is to be released, SCCS applies all the changes necessary to produce that version.

Module recompilers are designed for modular systems. If a change is made to one module, the recompiler monitors changes to modules, and automatically recompiles other modules affected by the change.

System browsers search for origins and purposes of particular modules, and logical links between modules. Software can be analysed for maintenance information. These tools can be enhanced by artificial intelligence.

Visibility enhancers display the structure of software, enabling cross-referencing and converting badly structured code into well structured code.

Effects of computer revolution

Although software reliability standards may be improving, the diffusion of computing equipment has led to a leap in the quantity of software being used. It is also being used in an increasingly decentralised manner. This means that whereas once a fault detected in one site might only have been in existence in another few sites, today it might exist in tens of thousands of sites. For micro software, the problem is technically easy to solve by exchanging disks. From a business perspective, the problem is more serious. A software fault means exchanging thousands of faulty disks, at some expense. Added to this is the great demand on the part of users for up-dates when new versions are issued (or a desire for an old version to be supported). A final complicating factor is the widespread use of software which is effectively a composite, consisting of pieces which have slowly been built up over many years.

Distribution channel problems

Technically, 'patching' software is not difficult for the original supplier (provided that the original programmers are still working for him!). When software reaches the customer via a tortuous route, perhaps through a sourcing agreement between software house and equipment supplier, and thence through a dealer, the situation is less simple. It is difficult for dealers to maintain standards of software support which customers feel entitled to. The situation may be aggravated by customers' failure to understand that software can be as unreliable as hardware. The 'you said it would do this' syndrome is all too common. The inability of software to perform as promised may not be so serious as software failure, perhaps triggered by operator error (incorrect key stroke sequence). In this case, the dealer may find it more difficult to deal with the problem. Legal liability may also arise, as vital data may be lost.

Easing software support problems

Steps to ease problems of software support include:

1. Maintaining a clear link with the original software producer. Since he may be in another continent, this does not necessarily mean a direct link. It does mean that at every stage of distribution, the problem escalation path should be clearly defined, along with responsibilities and liabilities. In many

cases, this may include the customer (who should be trained to reduce customer-error based problems). In microcomputers, where the operator may be a non-specialist (e.g. secretary, small businessman or manager), this is particularly important.

2. Creating an efficient and rapid escalation process. For microcomputers, this may be a software hot-line for customers or dealers. For larger systems, there may be an 'internal' hot line back to software source.

3. Ensuring that all those in the distribution chain are qualified to determine the nature of the problem, and route it to the appropriate destination for solution. This is not easy, but it is clearly right to train all those involved to diagnose the general nature of the problem.

4. Ensuring that all those involved receive regular bulletins to up-date them on software changes, fault diagnosis procedures, and anything else that may improve their ability to support software or avoid problems. This may extend to information on known bugs and how to remedy them (rather than by the supplier remedying them himself).

CHECKLIST FOR CHAPTER 4

General product design approach

* Does our approach to product design (revolutionary or evolutionary) match our technical and commercial position relative to our competitors?
* Do the frequency with which we redesign our products and the life for which our products are designed take into account the average customer life of our equipment?
* Does our equipment design take into account the need for serviceability?
* Have we considered how far we can take modularity in the design of our equipment, and whether there are any cases where very high reliability may make modularity unnecessary?

Life-time costs

* Do we follow the life-time cost approach in equipment design? If not, do we have good reasons for not doing so?
* Does our equipment design process use all the information from all relevant functions required to follow the life-time cost approach?
* Are all the information systems and flows (within and between functions) required to do this in place?
* Do appropriate staff in all relevant functions (including general management) understand the need for the approach, and are they motivated to follow it?
* Do targets, controls and incentives support the approach?
* Have we enumerated clearly all the categories of costs that are associated with the purchase and use of our equipment, whether they are borne by us or by our distributors or customers?
* Does the life time over which we evaluate costs correspond with that used by our customers? If not, have we evaluated the consequences of any difference from all functional perspectives?
* Have we a process for determining what feasible levels of life-time costs would be appropriate, given customers' and distributors' needs and our requirements for profitability?
* Does this process include inputs from relevant functions (e.g. finance, purchasing, quality control, marketing, design, development, production)?
* Do we calculate the end-of-life parts costs for our products accurately?

* Does our service pricing take into account end-of-life costs, as far as is possible given the competitive situation?
* Do we have a robust marketing policy for terminating products if end-of-life costs make them uneconomic to support, if we cannot obtain a service price which will cover true end-of-life costs?
* If we decide on marketing grounds to maintain products uneconomically, is the cost of this debited against the marketing function?

Automatic diagnostics
* Have we explored all the opportunities being opened up by microprocessor technology for introducing or extending automatic diagnostics?
* For higher value equipment, have we explored all opportunities being opened up by communications technology for introducing or extending remote diagnostics and/or repair?
* Have we investigated in detail the impact of automatic and remote diagnostics on our service force in the future, and are we planning to make any required changes in engineers staffing and training, and support and spares resourcing?

Quality
* Have we identified all the origins of inferior quality (ignorance, lack of integration, or indiscipline)?
* Have we identified all the appraisal, failure and prevention costs of inferior quality, whether incurred by ourselves (and in this case, in whatever function), our distributors or our customers?
* Have we identified all the consequences of these costs (whether immediate financial costs, marketing or strategic)?
* Have we tried a comprehensive approach to improving quality (quality audit or quality circles)?

Software products
* Have we applied all the above listed questions to our software design and production (covering identification of problems, through to assessing their full effect in terms of immediate and wider costs, to prevention of problems by more structured approaches to quality)?

5 MARKETING AND SERVICE

Marketing policies influence the service operation in two ways:

1. By supporting the marketing of service for a given installed base of equipment (e.g. by generating providing a strong company image, by providing good quality information on the needs of customers, by designing appropriate incentives for the sale of service contracts).
2. By ensuring that major marketing decisions take service aspects fully into account.

The first point is dealt with more fully in Chapters 2, 3, 6 and 7. The second point is the subject of this chapter. This more strategic contribution of marketing to service is most evident in the area of new product development and launch. The two are of course closely related. Successful marketing of new products often depends upon effective service.

New products and service

Research into new product success and failure (especially in higher technology sectors) confirms that key contributors to new product success include the depth of the relationship with the customer, management of the after-sales situation, and the extent of the effort made by the supplier to educate the customer. As the service function has an important 'custodial' role with respect to the customer, it can obviously play an important part in helping products succeed by cementing an in-depth relationship with the customer, in educating the customer, and in ensuring that after-sales service problems are minimised. The contribution of service to new product success implies that product development processes should pay more explicit attention to the role of service during the development process.

The staged product development process

In what follows, we sketch out one view of the stages of product development, the staged approach, and indicate what kind of service input is appropriate at particular stages. This process can be summarised in the following stages.

- Identification of opportunity.
- Evaluation of opportunity.

- Defining the product development goals and project.
- Development and testing.
- Introduction.
- Full marketing.
- Maintenance.
- Termination.

These stages are in principle sequential. Under certain circumstances it may be right for some parts of the project to run ahead of others. For example, if the product is a modification of an existing product, testing may be carried out as part of the evaluation of the opportunity. But 'leaping ahead' should be by specific exception. The opportunity evaluation and goal definition that follows may indicate that the modification should be different.

Identification of opportunity: Here, the proposal (which may be one of many under evaluation) is a broad business proposal, probably just a few pages. It should indicate clearly the key technical, cost and market factors which need to be researched more before evaluation can take place. There will be enough detail at this stage for the service implications of the opportunity to be discussed, as asset management requires. The technical and cost factors should incorporate estimates of reliability and serviceability.

Evaluation of opportunity: Here, market and technical data is combined to evaluate different opportunities. At this stage, service requirements will be sketched out broadly, with preliminary cost estimates.

Defining product development goals and project timetable: The supplier is not yet committed to proceed with the product, but detailed product objectives must be specified, in terms of technical and marketing goals. With reliability and preliminary marketing targets, it should be possible to forecast, at least roughly, the service demands likely to be made by the product. A project programme must be defined which will lead to goals being reached. At the end of this stage, resources are committed to take the product to launch readiness for launch. Functional (marketing, service, manufacturing) strategies relating to the product should be set out in functional strategy plans. The service strategy plan covers points such as:
- Field organisation and staffing.
- Distributor service support.

- The installation plan - location, complexity of equipment/systems.
- Training for customers, service staff, central technical support, distributors, managers, and other support staff.
- Service productivity.
- Product launch arrangements.

Development and testing: Here, the major investment of development funds takes place. At the end of this stage, the product is checked for launch readiness. A launch readiness test (Alpha test) may be run, to confirm that original technical goals have been attained. A similar test may be run on service, to test whether the required resources are in place to market the product.

Introduction: The product is put into production, while initial installations are made. Some investment in service resources and parts takes place. The product may still be terminated or delayed at this stage, if initial installations are unsatisfactory.

Full marketing: Production at 'mature' volumes starts, and after-sales service and support start to absorb resources and generate revenue.

Maintenance: The installed base reaches its peak, and new manufacturing ceases, although there may be some refurbishing, using new parts and parts stripped from scrapped equipment. No new installations are made. Service and other after-sales revenue peaks and starts to decline with the installed base. Follow-on products enter full marketing, to provide existing customers with viable replacements and new customers with a product to meet their needs.

Termination: The product is no longer supported by the supplier, although third parties may continue to support it.

Aim of the staged approach
The aim of setting out the stages of product development in this way is to identify the actions needed to get the product to market and keep it there profitably. Too many suppliers, in their haste to get a product to market, ignore some of the fundamental requirements mentioned above. Products have reached the market with parts that do not work, or without engineers to support them. A development process with a clear sequence of stages, and

reviews held at the end of each stage to confirm readiness for the next stage, may avoid this. It also makes application of asset management easier, since asset management criteria can be introduced at each review.

EFFECTS OF MARKETING POLICIES ON SERVICE COSTS

Equipment marketing policies have an important effect on service costs. In this section, we examine this effect, and consider how it is possible to pursue an integrated design, manufacture, marketing and service policy.

Installed base growth

The main effect of marketing policy on service costs is via the growth rate, extent of dispersion, and the life of the installed base of equipment. A marketing policy which creates a small, widely dispersed installed base which lives so long that special parts have to be ordered towards end of life will generate higher unit service costs than a policy which creates a large, concentrated and less long-lived installed base. In deciding elements of product launch strategy that affect the size, dispersion and life of the installed base, the effect on service costs should be taken into account. There may also be effects related to the service demanded by customers who constitute target markets. If they are all very demanding, but unwilling to pay a premium for a high level of service, service margins may be lower.

Different marketing options

We can distinguish a number of options for marketing. They include:

Spray and pray: This is unfocused marketing, to all customers that the sales force or distributors can find. This may produce a widely dispersed and small installed base, leading to high service costs. A further problem is that the distribution of the installed base will only emerge after marketing starts. This may result in the need for rapid redeployment of service resources.

Rifle shot: This involves selective pre-planned focusing on targets thought to be hot prospects for the product. If they are grouped geographically (e.g. in major urban areas), service costs may be much lower, and service resources can be allocated in advance to deal with these areas. The key principle of this option is that the best prospects are those who pay the best prices, or buy in the greatest volumes, so there should also be a good chance of charging a premium on service. This approach is more predictable. Products emerge fully supported and customer satisfaction may be high, as marketing and service resources are less likely to be stretched. The whole company focuses on satisfying a well-defined set of customers. But low production volumes and slowly growing installed base raises unit production and service costs.

A variation of this is to concentrate on the same segments, but focus product development on making each generation of products redundant. This can produce a stable customer base, so even if the installed base is geographically dispersed, it will be located with long established customers (who may have several generations of equipment at any one time). This will reduce service costs below what they would be if the equipment was with different customers.

MIRV: Extending the military analogy (the MIRV missile had Multiple Independent Re-entry Vehicles, which left the final stage of the missile to make their way to separate targets), this involves simultaneous pre-planned targeting of more targets than in the rifle shot approach, but addresses less market potential than the volume approach. The choice of targets depends not only on the sales or profit potential of individual targets, but also on the need to generate the volumes needed to achieve marketing, production and service economies of scale, and to prevent competitive entry into accounts with second-order potential. If the targets are clustered geographically, this can result in very favourable service costs, with a reasonably large installed base (keeping parts costs down), but not too widely dispersed.

Phased: This is a variation of the MIRV approach, except that the best targets are addressed initially, followed later by second and third order targets. This approach may be adopted (as opposed to MIRV) when:
  - It is difficult (e.g. due to constrained sales, management or production resources) to handle so many targets at once, or when the effectiveness of hitting targets depends on initial learning by sales staff.
  - When initial purchasers are likely to pay such a high premium relative to later purchasers that phased pricing yields more profit.
  - When production learning has a substantial impact on costs and feasible production volumes (a similar point may apply to service learning).

This approach can lead to an initially dispersed installed base, raising service costs (unless phasing is strongly geographic). Products may have a long active installation life, increasing service costs and complexity.

Volume: This aims to maximise sales subject to making absolute profit targets. High volume production and marketing and rapid increase in size and density of the installed base drive down production, marketing and service costs. Pre-planning consists of creating the capacity (production, marketing and service) to get the product to market and arranging with third parties (e.g. distributors, parts suppliers, third party service) to fill any product or resource gaps which might inhibit the approach. Unit production, marketing and service costs are lower than on any other approach, although initial absolute costs may be much higher. This approach builds a large customer base, easing the marketing of follow on products, and generates a very profitable after-market (e.g. supplies, parts). It requires acute cost control in all functions because of inherently lower margins. The rapid roll-out of the installed base may cause service and physical distribution problems, and lead to a surge in demand for after-sales support.

Combining options

Although each option has its weaknesses, these can often be removed by combining them with other options to remove weaknesses of options chosen. For example, a supplier constrained on marketing resources may use MIRV for major target segments, and spray and pray for less strategically important markets, to increase the total installed base and reduce service costs. Figure 5.1 gives a rough picture of how the installed base might grow under different options. These profiles would change if options were combined.

General effects on service

Here we consider some service and related factors which affect how the different options work. For products involving radically new use-concepts, user feed-back prior to full launch (e.g. by trial installations) or after launch can be crucial. The immediate post-launch period may be needed to establish equipment viability by installing it in technically sophisticated environments which are capable of handling initial problems. It may be right to follow a phased policy initially, with rapid roll out once it is clear that procedures for dealing with the product on a volume basis will actually work.

INSTALLED BASE

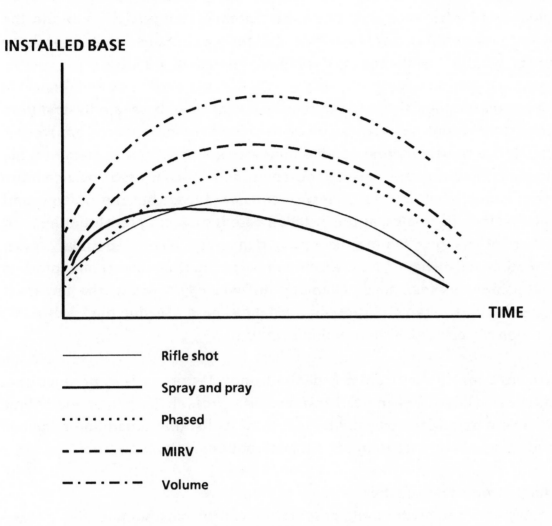

———————	Rifle shot
▬▬▬▬▬▬	Spray and pray
• • • • • • • • • •	Phased
– – – – – –	MIRV
– · – · – · –	Volume

Figure 5.1 Effects of different marketing policies

Non-volume options are all likely to have higher service costs, caused by more travel time and more expensive parts manufacturing or purchasing (either because they are bought in smaller quantities per year, or because they have to be stockpiled for the longer total life of the product). But this may be compensated for by being able to charge a premium on service (in all but the spray and pray options), since customer need for the equipment-service package should be greater, and the supplier's hold on the customer tighter.

In the volume strategy, the aim is to reach peak installed base rapidly, and then go on to the next product. A given model is in the field shorter, the parts stock is carried for a shorter period, and engineers service a narrower variety of equipment. Field upgrades are discouraged, with pricing used to encourage discontinuation of old products. Service costs are lower, but the training and installation load fluctuates, as the installed base is subject to revolutionary, not evolutionary change. Volume marketing demands a very responsive service organisation. It may have to run with more spare capacity, since if new product service parameters (e.g. field reliability) are wrongly forecast, the impact is multiplied by the rapidly growing installed base. Maintaining customer satisfaction can be hard with the volume option.

Service costs for different options depend upon factors such as product mix, product durability (i.e. expected installed life profile); length of marketing cycle; service parameters (reliability, nature of faults) that determine engineer workload; spare parts, training and support requirements.

The multi-product perspective
So far, we have dealt with single products. Of course, most suppliers have more than one product line. If the same service and parts operation is dealing with several product lines, the consequences for service costs of particular marketing policies will be modified according to the prospects of obtaining service economies over different product lines. But the general strengths and weaknesses of different approaches will still apply.

THE INTEGRATED APPROACH OF SOME JAPANESE SUPPLIERS
The design approach
In some Japanese companies, the lack of division between production and design engineering (usually working in a single location) ensures integration of

design and production decisions. Products are designed for volume manufacturing and marketing. This affects component standardisation and ease of assembly. To reduce service costs and increase service and parts profits, design takes into account life-time costs, rather than just equipment costs. There is a drive to reduce the number of parts in a product, to increase manufacturability and reliability (much unreliability is due to connections or interaction between parts). In doing this, Japanese companies explore substitutes for traditional materials to reduce the machining or assembly needed to produce a complex part and cut replacement costs. Whole product ranges may be designed simultaneously, with high commonality of parts between different products in the range. The cost of parts may be further reduced by the existence of very high volume parts manufacturers, who concentrate on supplying standard and special products (e.g. electronics, optics) to producers of particular kinds of equipment, but encourage their customers (who compete with each other) to use standard components as far as possible.

Marketing strategies

In many equipment markets, Japanese suppliers follow volume marketing strategies. A large installed base is created rapidly, often sold to and serviced by distributors (with the Japanese supplier taking the major profit on parts). After-market revenue (e.g. service, parts, supplies) to the supplier over the product life is often larger than original sales value. The cost of marketing to the existing customer is low (relative to the new customer). Brand loyalty may be higher than for the new customer (allowing a higher price to be charged on service and parts). So after-market profit margins are often much higher than on initial equipment sale. Most Japanese and Western companies have strategies to exploit this opportunity (e.g. substantial profit mark-up on service parts). But product design and the growth profile of the stock of equipment generated by their production and marketing policy combine to make Japanese companies' after- market profits particularly high, for reasons given below.

Design for life cycle performance and obsolescence

Western and Japanese design philosophies may differ. The Western product may be designed to last 10 years, with reasonable reliability (perhaps improving, due to 'field fixing'). The Japanese product may be designed to last 5 years, with initially high reliability, but a high failure rate towards end of life (see Figure 5.2). The user, choosing between the 'latest' Japanese technology at a claimed

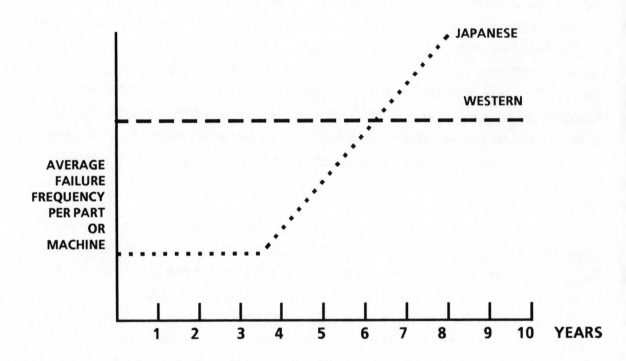

Figure 5.2 Failure frequency

higher reliability and Western machines of older design, finds it hard to choose the Western machine if he is indifferent to reliability after 5 years. Japanese choice of length of life is often determined by the period after which the average buyer replaces the product, taking into account obsolescence. There is no point in designing a product to last for 10 years if it will be obsolete within 5. This reflects the domestic Japanese tendency for rapid product replacement. Designing for limited but reliable life produces a cheaper product. The number of spares used in the product life is lower, as is repair frequency, especially if the Japanese supplier has succeeded in reducing the number of parts compared to the Western supplier.

Operating in a market with Western reliability profiles (e.g. frequent replacement with cheaper parts) makes it possible for the Japanese to charge a high parts mark-up. Customers may relate to the total service bill, not parts prices. When the 5 years (of the above example) is up, reliability may be a less relevant consideration in replacement than technical modernity. This reliability profile, and its associated cost and price advantages, make it crucial to ensure customers do replace equipment more often. This is done by ensuring that the latest technical developments are incorporated in all new products, rather than introducing them slowly at premium prices (a Western habit), and that products are as fully featured as possible.

Impact of design, marketing and production policy

Japanese policies lead to a particular age-profile of stock. Their new products are introduced frequently, build up to peak stock very quickly, and the stock then declines rapidly. The equivalent Western product will build up more slowly to peak stock, which declines less rapidly (due to much greater variability of scrappage time around the expected life of the product). But, to keep up with market development, the Western company may have to introduce new products nearly as frequently. This leaves Western companies with a more varied, older installed base, and a more complex and costly after-market (carrying parts, training service engineers, designing up-grades or add-on products to be compatible with as many existing machines as possible). It may be more inviting to third party after-market suppliers, who rely on a long tail of equipment to address. Parts piracy is discouraged by lack of a substantial and enduring stock of older, less reliable equipment.

One sign of the importance of this market is the investment made by many Japanese companies in developing a reliable and efficient worldwide parts logistics system. The profit made on the after-market permits a more aggressive policy on initial sale, while the very rapid initial build up of installed base means that the after-market grows to peak size earlier than in the Western interpretation of the market. This means that the optimum sized after-market operation can be developed at an early stage.

Implications

The service operations of Western companies in competition with Japanese suppliers need to drive home the message of asset management to design, manufacturing and marketing functions. Otherwise, Western suppliers risk making significantly lower profits on their service operations. In general, increased understanding of the relationship between service and other functions gives companies the opportunity to improve the effectiveness and perhaps profitability of customer service.

CHECKLIST FOR CHAPTER 5

* Is the service perspective on new product development and launch fully integrated with design, development and marketing perspectives?
* Is the contribution of service to new product success understood?
* Is the importance for service of total product range planning understood?
* Is relevant information from the service function (e.g. requirements as to reliability, serviceability, engineer skills, spare parts) input into new product decision and management processes at the right stages?
* Is a service strategy plan formulated at the same time as the marketing strategy plan?
* Are the service implications of different marketing strategies, arising from speed of installed base growth, installed base density, nature of installation, type of customer and type of use fully understood?
* Are the service benefits and costs of different strategies properly calculated?

6 THE SERVICE MIX: CUSTOMER SATISFACTION

In Chapter 1, three levels of service policy making were distinguished:
- Service objectives and strategy.
- Service mix.
- Service implementation and support.

Service objectives and strategy

The financial objectives of service are normally given by overall company objectives and strategy. For example, the prime objective of service may be to provide a loyal customer base, without making a loss, taking into account the cost of capital to finance service assets (especially parts). This may include as subsidiary targets 100% penetration of contracts for the supplier's own equipment (a share objective), while ensuring that cash flow is positive. On the other hand, the financial objective might be to earn a high margin to subsidise product sales, and a return on assets consistent with market rates.

The other three components of strategy, stance, customers and channels, are highly interdependent and closely related to marketing strategies and to the competitive situation. For example, if the supplier's objective in relation to equipment sales is to capture a high and loyal share of a large and rapidly growing market, then the resources of the service organisation may be stretched, particularly if marketing has absorbed most of the company's resources. A feasible objective for the service organisation may be to provide a good but basic service to all customers as efficiently as possible, seeking later to improve the level of service. In some cases, this may involve using third party channels for service, either because they are being used for sales anyway, or because they ease the strain on resources. Later on, service may be improved to defend the new large customer base.

The important point is that service objectives and strategy must be set explicitly. Suppliers who fail to do this may find that they are in trouble - often adopting a responsive stance in a market where being proactive pays.

The service mix

Service objectives and strategy have their outcomes in the form of a level of service as perceived by customers. This outcome is partly the result of technical and commercial service mix elements - product, price, promotion and distribution, applied to chosen customers. The relationship between the perceived level of service and the technical and commercial elements of service depends on the supplier's success in generating customer satisfaction. Customer satisfaction is a product in its own right. It must be consciously produced. We consider this product in the present chapter, and the technical elements of the service mix which go into supporting it in Chapter 7.

CUSTOMER SATISFACTION

Business success can be measured in many ways. We talk of products which are successful, companies which dominate markets, successful advertising campaigns, and so on. One crucial measure is success with customers. This is a simple idea, which adds an important perspective to policy. Success with customers consists of a number of elements, such as:

Number of customers

This may be an absolute number or a proportion of customers in the market. For companies used to measuring success by installed base of equipment, this number may be difficult to measure, particularly if the supplier sells a variety of different types of equipment. There may be no customer data base, but several different data bases arranged by product. Note that 'customer' is not necessarily identical with 'organisation' or 'establishment'. Customers include all buyers and users of equipment, and possibly even all those who depend on it! The number of customers may be very large, even if the number of paying customers is small. Whether non-paying customers are of concern depends upon the composition of the buying centre (Chapter 2).

Loyalty of customers

This is measured most simply by the probability of the customer buying from us again, whether renewal of a service contract, or purchase of additional or replacement equipment (to which service may be attached). Other measures of loyalty include the premium the customer will pay to buy from us as opposed to other suppliers, and the costs we have to incur (during our relationship with the customer and at the time of a purchasing decision) to persuade him to stay with us. Replacing customers is expensive. Since a customer may not give us all his business, another measure is our share of their total purchases - equipment and after-market (service, supplies, accessories, peripherals, additional services, software) customers give us.

Customer profitability

This depends on the costs of and revenue from supplying and servicing the customer. Loyalty is an important determinant of profit, especially if selling costs are high. Loyalty may also enable us to provide a lower average level of service, provided we respond better when the customer really needs it.

CUSTOMER ORIENTATION

After-sales service may be too equipment-oriented (servicing equipment, not the customer), just as a sales operation risks being too product oriented (selling the product, not marketing to the customer). The meeting point of sales and service is with the customer. The two may fail to meet because the company has not translated marketing objectives into customer objectives. This is one job definition for service, to keep the customers that are necessary for the company to fulfil its objectives, by managing the relationship with them at every level, from the equipment level to the human level.

The customer's view

Many suppliers assume that customers see the company exactly as an insider would, distinguish between product, technical service and all other after-market elements, and understand that responsibility for each of these elements belongs to different parts of the company. Customers may distinguish between engineer and company (often a sign of failure in customer relations, as the engineer should be a positive part of company image). They may distinguish less clearly between other elements of the relationship. Some customers expect to have similar (positive) relationships in all their dealings with the supplier. Failure in one aspect of the relationship (e.g. in getting a billing query settled) may lead to expectations of failure in other areas. So one of the first steps in specifying the "customer satisfaction product" is to understand exactly what level of care customers feel entitled to.

In consumer and small business markets, customers may expect to have care lavished upon them, even if they have spent small sums on product acquisition.

Rightness or wrongness is irrelevant - the supplier is seen as a large company which can afford to look after the customer. The key to successful service in these sectors is to recognise this, then generate the image of 'caring', while keeping a tight rein on service to ensure that customer satisfaction is delivered profitably. To do this, it is vital to research what customers consider the key elements of service to be and how well the supplier is rated on these elements. A housewife whose washing machine has ceased to work may consider customer service to consist of a quickly answered telephone, a service call which arrives close to the predicted time, irrespective of how far ahead that time is, and absence of a second call to replace a spare part. She may be happy with strong evidence that her problem is being dealt with. Immediate attention is often almost as good as immediate problem resolution.

Delivering customer satisfaction

Customer research can provide most of the data necessary to specify broadly what kinds of policy will produce increased levels of customer satisfaction. Delivering the level needed to secure the customer base can be made difficult by resource constraints. Many suppliers have discovered that customer satisfaction, like product quality, pays for itself in increased sales or reduced marketing costs. We need to take this into account and, if possible, measure it. In quality programmes, most benefits are financially measurable. This should be the case with customer satisfaction programmes.

Improving customer satisfaction is not difficult, but it may be harder to sustain improvement. The internal dynamics of many companies (not least the pressure for increased sales and efficiency) may militate against sustained improvement, despite its clear commercial benefits. Companies which try to solve their customer satisfaction problems by throwing resources at them are less able to sustain improvements, which more normally result from changes in attitudes and business orientation.

CUSTOMER SERVICE ORIENTATION

Customer satisfaction can be improved through customer service orientation (CSO) in the business. This means customer satisfaction is adopted as a key criterion for evaluating any policy or action. There are a number of ways to achieve CSO. Larger companies often use large, formal programmes, since they have to imbue very large numbers of staff with CSO. Record keeping needs to be more comprehensive, training more complete, and so on. In smaller companies, CSO may be inherently stronger, because it is clearer to everyone in the business how important it is to retain and develop customers. A major element in CSO is motivation of staff who deal with customers. In smaller businesses, staff identification with the business tends to raise levels of motivation.

Ways of improving CSO

Here, a number of ways of improving CSO are discussed. No company uses them all, but most companies could use some of them to good effect. These methods are divided into several categories, as follows:
- Organisation (structure and staffing).
- Training, incentives and motivation.
- Measurement and control.
- Information flows to and from customer.
- Technical, physical and commercial aspects of service delivery.

ORGANISATION

Dedicated customer service personnel

Some argue that allocating responsibility for CSO to particular staff leads to buck-passing ('It's not my responsibility, it's his!'). If the customer service job is a 'doing' job ('It's his job to ensure that customers are satisfied'), the buck may be passed. If the job is defined as a guiding, educating, motivating, and communicating job, aimed at increasing the delivery of customer satisfaction through other staff, the risk of buck-passing is reduced. Everything depends on the success of customer service staff in influencing staff who deal directly with customers. However many customer service staff there are, if all other staff in contact with customers make it clear that they see customers as a hindrance to doing business, customer satisfaction will not reach high levels. The ability of customer service staff to influence other staff depends partly upon company 'culture'. Companies which have always left their staff to get on with their jobs, while paying them according to simple measures of productivity (e.g. sales) may find it hard to get dedicated customer service staff accepted as influencers.

In large companies, the responsibility for customer care does not have to be centralised. Consistency does not necessitate centralisation. If major themes are dictated centrally, responsibility for applying them can be delegated to local levels, with the main controls being measures of customer care. To ensure that CSO is all-pervasive, it may be wise to appoint a senior manager with responsibility for CSO, with strong indirect authority, and reporting to the Board. This individual is responsible for:

- Communicating the concept and its benefits throughout the organisation, and monitoring the quality of customer care delivered.
- Ensuring that customer satisfaction criteria are used where appropriate.

He will tend to be involved in production quality control, parts policy, product life reliability analyses, customer surveys and complaints handling, producing reports of status of resolution of problems, product development statusing, and sales and service planning.

Responsibility for CSO at the right level

There are strong reasons for locating responsibility for customer satisfaction at the level of the customer (or as close to the customer as possible). This may be unsuccessful if staff dealing with customers have high turnover rates. Lack of continuity may destroy the required motivation. Even if turnover rates are low, procedures for handing over responsibility for particular customers between staff may be needed (especially for more important customers).

There is no point in making staff accountable for things they cannot control. If severe problems are caused by product quality, it may be difficult to distinguish these from customer care problems (though measurement systems are capable of doing this, particularly if they have been in place long enough to identify underlying trends in and causes of customer satisfaction). Service engineers are clearly not responsible for these problems. A more difficult example would be when the problem is caused by mismanagement of engineers. So results of customer surveys should always be analysed for connecting factors (e.g. shared first line management), they are treated as the responsibility of the individual member of staff.

Changing job titles

This may sound naive, yet in many cases "the title maketh the man". An account sales executive or equipment service engineer who:

- Becomes a customer account manager or customer service officer,
- Receives training which makes it clear that his job has changed, even if with the same customers and selling or servicing the same products,

- Is subject to different review criteria (e.g. including customer satisfaction measures) and processes,

may see the new title as confirming the changed nature of his task.

Management style

If internal company relationships are fairly negative (e.g. characterised by exploitation or lack of communication), staff may allow this to affect their relationships with customers. They may transfer the style directly, treating customers as they would a member of staff, or try to protect the customer from the worst excesses of the company. The latter may create (temporarily) satisfied customers and members of service staff, but may lead to problems when the customer is choosing whether to renew his relationship with the company (e.g. replacing or buying additional equipment). This situation is often revealed in customer satisfaction surveys when service engineers are rated highly, but sales staff or the company receive very low ratings.

The solution is to develop a management style which encourages staff to behave as if their colleagues were customers and suppliers, recognising mutual dependence, respecting their position, and using management, communication, negotiating and influencing skills to achieve results. This may amount to a cultural change, and take several years to achieve. The likelihood of success depends partly on whether the next point is addressed.

Approach to company planning

If the need for CSO is in some way "superimposed" upon the central planning and decision processes of the company, the chances of success are small. The need for CSO derives from a business need (e.g. to have a large, satisfied customer base). The focus on this need will (or should) arise from the company's main policy and planning processes (e.g. the business or marketing plan). The decision as to the nature of the solution (the way to achieve CSO) should also derive from these processes, and the implementation of the decision should be seen to be at least as important as the implementation of other, more 'normal', business and marketing strategies.

This may mean introducing CSO as an explicit element into strategy. The strategy should include the answers to such questions as:
- How many customers will we have in X years time?

- How satisfied do we want them to be?
- What will be the benefits to us of their satisfaction?
- What are we going to do to make sure they are satisfied?
- What will it cost us to achieve this?
- How will we know when we have achieved this?

TRAINING, INCENTIVES AND MOTIVATION
Personal skills training
Despite the slight cynicism sometimes attracted by the 'Have a nice day!' approach, much can be done to develop personal skills to improve customer satisfaction, particularly in areas such as:
- Listening.
- Complaints handling.
- Calming customers, and lowering tension levels.
- Telephone answering.
- Voice quality.
- Checklist use in diagnosing problems and in responding to queries.
- Letter writing and reading.

Skills should be focused on delivering the right message, avoiding the 'who sold you this, then' or 'we're having this problem with all our machines', or 'you should have bought a better model (or worse) someone else's model'. Customers may see service engineers as independent experts with a special ability to judge whether the right purchase has been made. Their training in customer relations should ensure that they:
- Reinforce the correctness of the customer's decision.
- Confirm that the engineer would have done the same thing if he had been in the customer's position.
- Avoid statements reflecting negatively on the way the customer has used the equipment.
- Avoid comment on whether the particular product is generating many similar problems.
- Avoid running down any previous service engineer.

Role play is useful in this kind of training (with roles including customer, engineer, line management and customer relations staff).

Complaints handling
Complaints handling may be a sensitive issue. Here, training should cover:

- Empathising with the customer.
- Creating a positive atmosphere.
- Generating warmth and friendliness.
- Protecting the company from legal action.
- Protecting the image of the company.
- Being objective.
- Getting the facts - separating fact from fiction.
- Co-ordinating with other departments.
- Using information gathered from complaints.
- Ensuring no dangerous precedents are set.
- Demonstrating positiveness in face to face discussion, via body language, taking notes, and so forth.

Training packages

Various suppliers are marketing high quality packages which enable companies to train engineers and support staff with mimimum waste of time or resource. One of the best of these is 'Effective Customer Service', from Scandinavian Training Systems. This programme is based on the principle that the engineer must service the customer as well as the equipment. The engineer sees the customer when the latter is at his most vulnerable. He must understand the customer and be able to handle non-technical problems. The package includes:

1. Understanding the customer's situation and psychology.
2. Physical handling of the situation.
   - Engineer's manner, dress and appearance.
   - Working in an orderly fashion.
3. Balanced conversations with the customer.
   - Obtaining relevant information from the customer.
   - Learning how to listen.
   - Avoiding technical language.
   - Avoiding strong statements.
   - Avoiding allocating blame to the customer or engineer's company.
   - Creating a feeling of confidence.
4. Presenting the advantages of the relationship.
   - Explaining the benefits of how the equipment is being serviced and of particular steps in the service.
   - Dealing with objections.

5. Handling sales opportunities.
   - Recognising buying signals from the customer.
   - Recognising opportunities for a sale.

Staff suggestion schemes

These may improve customer and staff satisfaction, but should be used with care. They may produce costly wish-lists. Implementing suggestions (and publicising implementation) is vital for success, so unrealistic suggestions can be damaging. Guidelines should be issued as to what the company is looking for, stressing that the objective is to improve customer satisfaction and profit. Accepted suggestions should be publicised amongst staff and customers. Rejected suggestions must be handled with clear explanations of why they are not feasible.

Identification with the business

If staff who handle customers behave as if customers are their own private customers, customer service is likely to improve. If staff fail to identify with the business, it is hard to improve customer satisfaction. Identification with the business may be achieved through management style (a family identification) or financial incentives (see below).

Financial incentives

Corporate success can be linked in an overall manner with staff success, or more directly related to an individual's specific part in success with customers e.g. satisfaction of particular customers, sales deriving from a lead obtained. Rewards may include stock options, profit-sharing, retirement incentives, pay incentives, and career progression.

Internal publicity

Success stories relating to customer satisfaction should be published within the company, whether they result from individual or company-wide initiatives. These are part of the internal communication used to stimulate and maintain motivation, and serve to humanise the idea of customer satisfaction. These stories should normally feature named individuals in customer organisations.

MEASUREMENT AND CONTROL
Customer-related measures of success
Most functions that deal with customers have to have success measures relating to company financial objectives. Sales staff usually operate with revenue or profit targets (whether or not their pay is affected by success is irrelevant - their job and promotion may depend upon it), and service engineers may have a target number of calls. Customer related success measures can be difficult to superimpose, as staff may perceive conflict between the two measures. This conflict may be very real (e.g. between short term economies of service, and the longer term need to retain customers). Line management has a key role in communicating the need for both sets of measures, and in managing staff so as to balance achievement between the two. The job of line managers is made easier if supported by clear company-wide communication of the need for both kinds of success. Non-financial customer-related measures of success include:

- Complaints reduction.
- Complimentary communications received by customers.
- Decrease in problems requiring higher level resolution.
- Speed of problem solving.
- Customer loyalty measures (e.g. repurchasing).
- Customer satisfaction ratings.

Quality control
The first requirement for the adoption of quality techniques in service is agreement on measures of service quality. On the technical side, this is not a problem, as much technical service is similar to manufacturing. Relevant measures include the proportion of jobs which have to be re-done within a specified interval and level of availability of parts. For customer service, the situation is different. Customer perception of service quality is at least as important as technical quality. If a customer satisfaction measurement system has been in place long enough, then the statistical base for a customer service quality programme exists. Customers who are dissatisfied with service as a whole, with particular aspects of service, or with particular service events (calls, etc.) can be identified, the causes traced, and the weaknesses rectified. If no measurement system is in place, then it must be created. All quality techniques depend on the availability of such data.

Internal communication

Good internal communications are vital in ensuring that customer problems are dealt with quickly. Communications are likely to be poor in companies using antiquated information processing or communications technology, or top heavy management reporting structures, without enough delegation.

Systems to diagnose problems

Reporting and recording systems should provide the data to identify causes of problems, as a first step to removing them. Often, data on reliability is averaged (e.g. mean time between failure, average response time), when real customer problems are caused by the extremes, which should also be reported.

Customer-oriented information systems

Equipment-based records are clearly needed for feedback to manufacturing and design. Customer-based records (covering equipment records, correspondence, etc.) are needed to identify customers with recurring problems (with whatever equipment). This information should be readily available for staff dealing with recurrences of a problem. This is important for small businesses, who try to avoid record keeping (or keep records in their owners' heads!).

Follow-up procedures

Follow-up procedures should ensure progress and check customer satisfaction with how any problems are resolved. This may include managers or staff telephoning, visiting or writing individually to establish the position. Even reply paid postcards yield useful evidence on perceived service quality. Service actions should only be considered complete when the customer has had his satisfaction restored to the level before any incident, not when the call has been scheduled or made.

Prioritising customers

General guidelines may prevent local service branches of large companies being sensitive to the relative needs of different customers. There are clearly times when a customer's need for service is urgent, and other times when it is not. Automatic procedures for allocating engineers according to size of customer, contract status or type of equipment may cause a branch to lose the flexibility which a small business might have, in the interests of 'efficiency' of the service operation. Yet the service operation lives or dies according to whether customers are satisfied. Some tolerance may need to be built into targets to allow for this flexibility.

INFORMATION FLOWS TO AND FROM CUSTOMER
The relationship with the customer

No company is flexible enough or can afford to meet all its customers' needs. Customer needs may be unpredictable (in type or timing), so the customer should be provided with help in getting the best out of service. This includes not only simple access to service, and various instructions, but also bulletins on how other customers get the best out of service, and personal contact with those who manage service staff (so the customer knows who to contact). Consider how much of what an insider needs to know to provide service should also be known by a customer who is trying to receive service. A formal communications programme may be needed to ensure that customers understand how the supplier handles its relationships with customers, what a service involves, how calls are handled, how spare parts are provided, how complaints are dealt with, how customer service is organised, and so on.

Personalising the company

Many customers like to feel they are being dealt with individually. If they never realise that individuals are responsible for providing service, it is not surprising if they take a jaundiced view of efforts to make them feel more satisfied with service. The supplier can improve matters by personalising its interface with the customer, by informing him who is responsible for service, and even issuing pictures and personal background information, to give credibility to the personal approach.

Communicating customer service efforts

Publicity given to efforts to ensure customer satisfaction should refer to respected customers who are willing to declare their satisfaction with service. Publicising success stories relating to customer satisfaction implies being honest about why the service was required, and not sweeping problems under the carpet. The risks of honesty are few - not many customers believe equipment or suppliers to be perfect! One way of supporting this kind of communication is by maintaining a testimonial file covering satisfaction with service as well as with products. It goes without saying that customers should be given the opportunity

114

to say whether they think they have received the level of service that is being publicised.

Customer suggestion schemes
These may be used as an adjunct to customer satisfaction questionnaires ('Is there any way in which our service might be improved?'). They may yield very valuable ideas and indicate more precisely areas in which improvements are required. The customer may know so little about how service is delivered that he cannot really make any useful suggestion (this is a good reason for being more open about the process). If such a scheme does bring results, it may be beneficial to involve prime customers in the implementation of any changes.

Outcome of previous calls for service
There are few worse signs of lack of customer orientation than when a supplier does not remember when and why the last call for service was made, and how it was resolved. Modern computing methods allow such data to be stored and accessed cheaply and easily.

Customer satisfaction surveys
We have already considered most aspects of these. If such surveys are used as a quick fix, the continuity needed to isolate trend changes will be absent, and the quality of the survey may be low (we may have the wrong respondent). These surveys should be treated as empanelment for customer research. We must check we have the right individual(s) from the customer organisation, that they have the motivation to respond, and that their response is unambiguous.

Realism on product performance
Customers should be given a realistic picture of product performance. They may stay with a product whose reliability has been exaggerated during the selling process, but are less likely to purchase from the same company again.

Keeping the customer informed
The customer may want (whether or not he asks for it) to be kept informed of the progress of the call, possible delays in engineer arrival, in obtaining a part, in return of equipment taken in for repair, and so on. Customers may want a definite estimate of when equipment will be restored to use, and be happiest of all when the estimate is accurate. If the estimate was optimistic, they may

appreciate honest communication of the reason why (provided it does not happen too often!). This implies keeping a record of call status, so a customer who telephones to inquire of progress can obtain this information.

Taking the initiative

Some service organisations are reactive, waiting for customers to call them when a problem occurs. It may be better to initiate attempts to discover customer problems (on the grounds that little, soluble problems become big, insoluble ones if left to develop). If this applies to the equipment being serviced, preventive maintenance is normally the solution. Preventive maintenance can be applied to the relationship between supplier and customer!

Correspondence and telephone expertise

Letter-writing can be a powerful aid to improving customer satisfaction. Having standard customisable letters for dealing with complaints, for resolving problems, or for thanking customers, can make communications easy and painless. The same can apply to telephone call scripts!

TECHNICAL AND PHYSICAL ASPECTS OF SERVICE DELIVERY
Reliable and serviceable products

Customer satisfaction depends partly on the product's reliability, ease of use and ease of service (which includes parts availability). Some customers do not distinguish clearly between the product and service. However, it is the customer's perception of the product that counts. The service organisation may be able to improve this by how they relate to the equipment while servicing it (e.g. comments made, treatment of equipment).

Avoiding customer disservice

Servicing equipment should not be a disservice to the customer (e.g. by spreading oil in a clean area, by calling at inconvenient times, or by giving unrealistic call back intervals).

COMMERCIAL ASPECTS OF SERVICE DELIVERY
Providing compensation

If the level of service has fallen well below customer expectations, it may be appropriate to give some kind of compensation to the customer, not necessarily in money, but in ways which will make the customer feel special, receptive to explanations, and forgiving. These include invitations to special events, entertainment by service managers, or a higher future level of customer service. In some cases, inconvenience may have been personal, not organisational, so the compensation should also be personal.

Segmenting service policy

The suggestions made in this chapter should not be applied indiscriminately. Customers can be segmented according to their needs for service or according to how they perceive service. Different policies will pay off with different kinds of customer. This applies not only to service contracts and prices, but also to customer relations policy. Some customers may like personal treatment, others not. Customer research, the sales force and service staff have an important role to play here in providing the data necessary for segmentation.

Allowing late buy-ins

Some companies refuse customers the right to buy into service when they originally opted out on purchase of the equipment. This buy-in should normally be permitted, by providing an inspection service. A customer regained is a sales opportunity for more products and service. Late admission to service contracts may be the cheapest way of acquiring a customer.

Realistic cost estimates

For non-contractual service, realistic repair costs and times should if possible be given before repair (without commitment), plus information on which the estimate is based (likely faults). Some suppliers offer flat-fee service for regular maintenance, provided that no major additional work needs carrying out. Rates should be published if possible. After repair, an itemised account should be given of the costs and their allocation (particularly of labour). All this requires clear policy on service costing.

SERVICE THROUGH DEALERS

Service may be provided with the involvement of third parties, often dealers for the product, but sometimes accredited service agents. In this case, whatever the division of labour between manufacturer and dealer (ranging from the dealer carrying out the full service, to the dealer passing the product back to the manufacturer), the principles of customer-orientation are doubly important. The dealer himself is a customer, who needs help in dealing with his customers.

Satisfaction of the final customer has to be achieved not via control, but indirectly, via influence, training, financial incentives and negotiation. The development of training material which is easy for the dealer to use is particularly important - he may not have much time to train himself or his staff, and needs that special extra incentive to do it professionally.

Particular emphasis must be placed on communication (in both directions) since the dealer is a separate entity. This communication is unlikely to succeed if it is only paper-based - field visits are essential. Reports on reliability will only come back from dealers if they feel they have an interest in providing them. This is only likely to be so if the total sales and service package offered to them encourages the passing back of data. Communication of policy direction, new product launches, and so on, should be personal, to encourage this orientation. Clarity on the liability position, during and after the warranty period, is also important.

CUSTOMER SATISFACTION PROGRAMMES
Customer satisfaction may be a problem in two situations:

1. Where customer satisfaction has more or less deliberately been ignored because of other priorities. For example, in a rapidly growing company, generating new customers may be the most important source of income. Resources may not be available for managing the interface with existing customers. In some cases, the company ignores customer satisfaction because it does not have the skills to deal with it, or because it does not recognise it as a problem.
2. Where customer satisfaction is accepted as an objective, but the way in which the company works (control systems, organisation, motivation) prevents it being dealt with effectively.

In the first situation, not taking any major steps to improve customer satisfaction may be the correct policy. It may be sufficient to continue to monitor satisfaction levels, and take some of the obvious but inexpensive steps on a 'maintenance basis'. These steps may relate to communication with the customer. But it will still be worthwhile undertaking preparatory work, by considering what actions will need to be taken in the future to deal with problems in this area. As soon as income from existing customers starts to reach significant proportions, these actions must be initiated. The problem is that companies in the first situation tend to become companies in the second situation, because they did not deal with customer satisfaction early enough.

In the second situation, even if customer satisfaction is a prime objective, a company may not understand its determinants. It may assume service response time to be a prime component of customer satisfaction. This is not uncommon, since companies often assume that internal engineer control criteria - of which response time is commonly one - are as important to customers as to the company. A survey might show uptime to be more important. The policy emphasis in these cases needs to be broadened from call handling processes and engineer resourcing to include machine reliability, availability of parts, prompt diagnosis, and so on. Service contracts need to be based on uptime, not response time, differentiation.

The first step in dealing with a general customer satisfaction problem is to ensure (perhaps via customer survey) that customer needs are understood (both technically and in the language the customer uses to express his technical requirements). The way the company administers the customer interface and provides service may not permit customer satisfaction objectives to be met. Administration may be inflexible, contracts complex, or field service managed with very different objectives. In these circumstances, improving customer satisfaction is rarely achievable overnight.

KEY STEPS IN CUSTOMER SATISFACTION PROGRAMMES

The key steps in improving customer satisfaction are:

1. Identify every point at which the company has an interface with the customer. There is room for an external perspective here - the customer's perception of the location of interfaces is as important as the company's. There may be interfaces which are unknown to the company, and ones known to the company that are not important to the customer. Some of this information will be produced by the customer survey.
2. Survey existing customers to discover their needs. This survey should be carried out independently, and differentiate between long-established customers and new customers, customers of different company services and products, and customers of competitive products. Small group discussions may be required to discover the language of customer satisfaction that

applies in the market in question, before undertaking more structured research.

3. Understand how the company performs at each of its customer interfaces, and what the customer would like to see at each of these interfaces.

4. Identify benefits that would accrue to the company if it could improve its performance at the customer interface (e.g. increased business, easier sale of expected increased business, reduced loss of business, higher prices obtainable due to improved performance, image)

5. Identify blocks to improving performance relative to customer needs (structure, control processes, motivation, staff skills, etc.), and the costs of removing them.

6. Identify which of the techniques listed in this chapter would be best for improving customer satisfaction.

7. Work out costs and benefits of implementing the chosen techniques, and put into place a process to handle that change. This process may well consist of at least as much internal campaigning, communications, and training as structural, process and other more visible kinds of change. The process may take a number of years, so foresight pays. If a problem is seen to be emerging, and its causes tracked down, then it may be possible to deal with it more cheaply now than waiting until it becomes serious enough for senior management to consider a formal 'customer satisfaction' programme to be necessary.

If the programme succeeds, it should make itself redundant as a distinct programme, since a key objective of any good customer satisfaction programme is to get delivery of customer satisfaction to become a 'way of life'.

CHECKLIST FOR CHAPTER 6

* Do we fully understand the interrelationship between technical measures of level of service, levels of satisfaction experienced by customers, and the individual elements of the service mix (products, prices, etc.)?
* Does our company have a robust set of objectives relating to success with customers (as opposed to success with products or with finances)?
* Do we understand how the different measures of success with customers relate to each other and to our company's overall success?
* Is the contribution of service to these measures of success recognised by general management and by the marketing function? If not, has the service function taken steps to establish the precise nature of its contribution and to communicate it to general management and marketing?
* Does our perception of what constitutes a successful relationship with a customer correspond to what the customer might think?
* Do our customers and our views of the role of service in this relationship differ?

Organisation factors
* Do we know who is responsible for our relationship with customers, and for its success? Have we decided the responsibilities of the service function in this respect?
* Is it right to give responsibility to a particular senior manager?
* If so, have we decided how he should execute his responsibility (e.g. by command, motivation, influence, communication)?
* Do titles of relevant staff reflect their responsibility for customers?
* Is management style conducive to good relations with customers?
* Do the company business, marketing and service planning processes focus adequately on customer satisfaction (e.g. by the use of appropriate measures of customer success and customer satisfaction, understanding of the benefits to the company of improving customer satisfaction, adoption of policies to improve it and controls to ensure achievement)?

Training, incentives and motivation
* Does training of relevant staff cover all the techniques which can be used to improve relationships with customers?

* Do our complaints-handling procedures ensure that each complaint is handled with minimum distress to and maximum reinforcement of relationship with customers?
* Are staff suggestion schemes used?
* Have we ensured (either via management style or financial incentives) that all our staff identify strongly enough with the business to treat our customers as their customers?
* Do we communicate to our staff success stories relating to customer satisfaction?

Measurement and control

* Have we investigated different customer-related measures of success, and chosen one or more that seems suitable to our particular business?
* Do all our managers and staff understand the importance of success with customers, and how generating customer satisfaction relates to their own success and that of the company in general?
* Have we considered applying quality techniques to our relationships with customers?
* Are problems in relationships with customers detected early, communicated and dealt with quickly?
* Do our information systems contribute to improving customer satisfaction, by helping us track significant general and specific causes of problems, and providing the information necessary to solve them? Do they normally report any variables which are directly related to customer-satisfaction?
* Are procedures for following up customers' problems of a high standard, and are they observed?
* Do we prioritise customers by the intensity of their need for actions to improve customer satisfaction?

Information flows

* Do we provide the customer with all the information he needs to get the best service out of our company?
* Is our company personalised to customers, so they know who is responsible for their service, and what has to be done by these people to deliver service to them?
* Do we communicate to our customers the general and specific efforts we make to ensure that they remain satisfied?

* Are we willing to take suggestions from our customers as to how to improve our service? Do we run a suggestions scheme? Do we publicise cases where customers' suggestions have been implemented?
* Do we take the initiative to discover whether any customers are experiencing problems with our service?
* Do we obtain regular reports on the state of customer satisfaction?
* Do we keep customers informed of the progress of their calls?
* Do we exercise all relevant correspondence and telephone skills to keep the customer informed, and to reinforce relationships before and after service calls?

Technical and physical aspects
* Do we understand how customers' satisfaction with a product can be improved by the halo effect of good service?
* Do we ensure that disservice to the customer is minimised during service (timing of call, minimum disruption, cleanliness, etc.)?

Commercial aspects
* Are we ever prepared to compensate the customer (or the individual within the customer's organisation) who has suffered from bad service?
* Do we ensure that the service we deliver is attuned to the differing needs of market segments?
* Do we allow customers who earlier opted out of a service contract to buy in later on?
* Do we provide realistic cost estimates, in the case of non-contractual service?

Service through dealers
* Do we ensure, via appropriate communication, motivation and training, that our dealers are in a good position to ensure that their customers are satisfied?
* Do we treat our dealers as customers in their own right?

7 THE SERVICE MIX: PRODUCT AND PRICE

Service is a product, or rather, many products. Within the overall product of customer satisfaction, ways of packaging service into products include variety of contracts, prices, and modes of contact. Many rules that apply to equipment product development also apply to service product development. This statement is clearly true in classic service industries (e.g. hotels, finance), but less so in a technical service operation. This may be because the common view that service makes up for deficiencies in equipment produces a feeling that to package service into a number of products and market them, is unfair to the customer! However, packaging and marketing of service products benefits the customer by giving him a wider choice of products, while the clarity of policy produced by this approach leads to a better level of service being delivered.

The standard product development process involves:
- Understanding market needs and the competitive situation.
- Understanding what products can feasibly be delivered.
- Devising product options to match market needs to what is feasible.
- Filtering out options which seem unlikely to meet commercial criteria.
- Devising a marketing mix for each option.
- Testing and evaluating the different options.
- Choosing one or more options.
- Launching the service product.

In many service operations, the product development process could be improved. Market needs are not well understood. Little creativity is applied to devising product options, so one option often has to be chosen out of one! Products are not marketed, but are simply passed to the sales or service force to sell.

The dimensions of service product that can be combined into a package are well known (see below). It is how they are combined, packaged and marketed that is likely to distinguish them. Some products may be designed to appeal to all users, delivering a level of service which is apparently much higher than other companies deliver (e.g quoting 99% uptime instead of 4 hour response time, despite the fact that the latter may involve a technically higher level of service).

124

Some products may be designed to appeal to customers who need a particular element of service (niche products). The objective of the process is to develop products which either tie the customer more firmly to the supplier, or apparently deliver a better level of service than competition. Note that, in specifying the service product, we need to specify what customers will perceive the service product to be, and what values they will perceive the product to yield. These perceptions determine whether they will buy it and how much they will be prepared to pay for it.

SERVICE PRODUCT OPTIONS

The service product may have almost as many dimensions as the hardware it supports. The product may be differentiated by:

- Up-time target or guarantee.
- Response time target or guarantee.
- Fast or simple access to service (e.g. 'hot line facility').
- Bring-in or pick-up service for portable equipment.
- Guaranteed preferential treatment for service calls.
- Maintaining a parts stock on site.
- Engineer dedicated to an individual or a group of customers.
- Skill or quality of engineer.
- Preventive maintenance.
- Back-up equipment.
- Equipment swap.
- Operator training to carry out service.
- Price.
- Contract length.
- Whether service carried out by supplier or distributor.
- Terms of payment.
- Compensation if level of service below guarantee.
- Labour only.
- Materials only.
- Non-contractual options.
- Bundling with hardware supply.

Within each option, there are additional options. If preventive maintenance is offered, how often will the call be? Given an initial contract price, will the price fall over time? Which service products should be offered depends on:

- The demand that exists or can be created for a particular product aspect. This is determined by how many customers demand it, and the strength of their need for it (usually indicated either by willingness to pay a premium or by loyalty to the supplier so long as it is supplied).
- The costs of supplying that aspect.

Particular (e.g. more profitable) service products can be promoted more heavily. Service can be promoted generically, but this has the same problems of general product or image advertising. Its results are difficult to measure, and it is unlikely to be effective if inconsistent with overall company image.

EVALUATING PRODUCTS

In evaluating different service products, we can apply techniques used to evaluate equipment products. The main approaches are:

- Strategic.
- Financial.
- Factor weightings.

The strategic approach

This ties product evaluation closely to corporate strategy. Company strategy may require that certain products be marketed. We may have decided that one of our corporate strengths is the ability to offer service on an international basis. We may have to offer service in all countries, even though in some countries we may have to sustain a loss in so doing.

The financial approach

This treats product choice decisions as financial decisions. Each product option is summarised as a set of forecast financial flows, such as:

- Incremental revenue generated by the product.
- Incremental costs of selling and implementing the product.
- Other investments (e.g. inventory).
- Cash flow and related debit/credit effects.

Though we may find it difficult to estimate how many contracts of a particular kind we can sell, our service market research should provide us with some basis for an estimate. The flows are then condensed into an estimated profit stream arising from the service product. This is reduced to a single figure by taking the net present value of the profit stream. This approach can underplay the strategic importance of product policy, particularly with respect to competitive strategy. We may have to provide a particular option because one of our competitors is using a similar option to win sales from us.

The factor weightings approach
This approach is used as follows:
- List the factors which are important for success.
- Weight the factors by their relative importance in determining success.
- Score each product according to its rating against each of these factors.
- Add the total up for each product.
- Rank the products by their scores.

Factors used in the weightings approach
The factors that may be included in the weighting approach are:

Financial - some combination of the measures listed above.

Service resources - whether the product can be delivered using existing service staff and other resources.

Competitive / strategic - whether absence of the product would expose us to strategic or competitive risks, and whether having the product would be more valuable to us than the revenue from it indicates (e.g. if it is likely to deliver a high level of customer satisfaction and a closer relationship with the customer, which would have a direct benefit in product sales.

THE PLANNING PROCESS
The quality of planning and execution of service product line change varies from company to company. Some companies simply guess, on the basis of minimal information, that customers want a certain service product and that the costs of producing it can be more then recouped from the likely revenue, and then line up the resources to supply and sell that service product, with little assessment of the product's impact on overall financial or business performance. Other companies go through all the stages of research, assessment and implementation quickly and thoroughly.

However formal the process by which service product decisions are made, it must be a truly integrated one. The impact of any change on all the functions or departments within the company and on all measures of success must be identified as part of the process. Key problem areas here tend to be in the areas of overhead cost allocation, of overlapping markets for new and old service products, and interdependence between hardware and service marketing.

PREVENTIVE MAINTENANCE

A typical service product decision is whether to offer preventive maintenance (PM) (defined as maintenance to ensure that equipment remains in working order, as opposed to corrective maintenance, undertaken to restore equipment to working order). The decision whether to supply PM is in theory not difficult to take. The problem lies in obtaining the information required to make it. The costs of PM rise and the direct and indirect (e.g. loss of output, higher process costs) costs of corrective maintenance fall in proportion to the level (i.e. frequency, comprehensiveness) of PM (see Figure 7.1). There may be some indirect costs due to PM (e.g. temporary stoppage of equipment). Given the reliability profile of the equipment, it should be possible to find a minimum total cost, determined by a particular level of PM. The financial calculation must be supplemented by estimates of other benefits, such as improved customer satisfaction (though this can be damaged by badly managed or mistimed PM), predictability in scheduling of customer operations around equipment availability, improved morale among the service force and with the customer, and a higher level of safety. Increased customer satisfaction may be transformable into a financial benefit via price.

Simple equipment

In equipment with only one component requiring maintenance, testing will give a failure profile (typically a distribution of expected failure around a mean time between failure). The curves drawn below would then reflect optimum maintenance scheduling. This optimum level would be calculated taking into account all the above costs, and the empirically established probability of failure. This would then need to be modified in various ways. The cost of travel to some equipment might be so high that PM would never pay. The indirect costs of failure will vary according to the customer, and these may have marketing consequences for the supplier. Some equipment is such that its effectiveness declines steadily until it fails, rather than experiencing sudden and catastrophic failure. Indirect costs may start to be incurred as soon as effectiveness falls, so this needs to be modelled too.

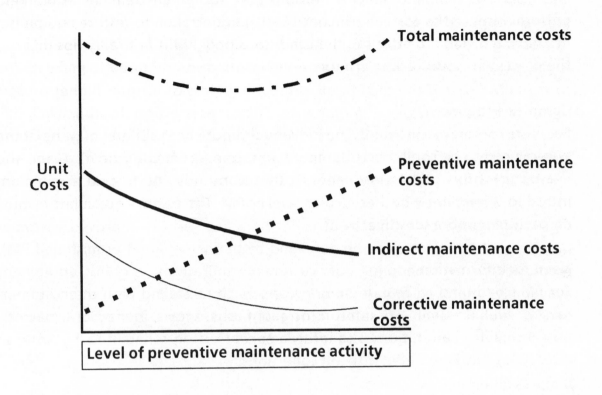

Figure 7.1 Preventive maintenance costs

This information should then be combined with information about maintenance resource availability (typically labour and parts), in order to schedule optimum PM patterns. PM usually eases the job of scheduling, as it reduces the number of corrective maintenance situations (inherently less predictable), while preventive work can be scheduled between corrective work. PM calls also lead to clearer information being yielded on equipment performance, as its state is documented more regularly, and more careful attempts are made to establish the conditions under which it fails. This may aid the process of modification to improve reliability.

Complex equipment

For more complex equipment, the individual failure probabilities of parts of the system need to be combined in a simulation exercise for the whole system, and the optimisation calculation carried out accordingly. Additional dimensions introduced here are whether to carry out PM on the entire equipment or only on particular (more sensitive) parts.

Need for information

For PM scheduling to be carried out properly, the installed base of equipment must be well documented, in terms of geography, access, indirect failure costs, post-installation alterations and local factors affecting reliability - e.g. intense duty cycles, working under difficult conditions.

TEST MARKETING SERVICE PRODUCTS

The difficulty of assessing a service product before taking the final go/no-go decision may be reduced by test marketing. This normally applies when one or two variants are to be assessed (if more than one variant is being tested, then different areas may be used to test different variants). Test marketing may be an expensive way of getting research information (particularly if the test fails) or a way of getting early profit and of sorting out problems prior to full launch. Test marketing should be set up in the same way as any other research process, with full awareness of what is being researched, what decisions will be made according to different outcomes of the test, and what key measures are to be used to judge whether to go ahead with full marketing. The main problems of test marketing are:

1. Once the company has gone through the pain of launching a particular service product, an inevitable management pressure builds up to launch

nationally, even if the results do not justify it. Results may often be distorted by optimistic interpretation in order to justify proceeding.

2. Despite a company's best efforts, the area chosen for test marketing may not prove to be an adequate basis for generalisation. This risk is particularly great with really innovative products, where the target buyer's behaviour may not be well understood.

3. The conditions of full-launch may be hard to approximate in test market. The service organisation may take time to adjust to a new way of working.

4. Pricing policy in the test may not be adhered to later on. In principle, it should replicate the likely pricing policy for the main launch.

PRICING SERVICE PRODUCTS

Price is a key determinant of service profit. Cutting price without a corresponding fall in unit costs (e.g. via higher volume) reduces profit margin. A price rise without a compensating incentive to the customer can cause reduced sales, unused service resources and inventory accumulation. Despite this, many companies under-research pricing, and fail to give price decisions enough priority. Price may be handled by the finance function on a cost basis. At the other extreme, pricing can be too close to what the market wants, without any attempt to sell a premium, irrespective of costs. Price is part of the service mix. It is substitutable for and by other elements of that mix, such as the packaging of service into different products, and supplier image.

The need for information

A key requirement for good pricing decisions is information about customer responsiveness to price changes, both absolutely and relative to:

- Other elements of the service mix.
- Competitors' policies.

Good pricing decisions are unlikely without knowing how price works to get or lose business, yet this is often neglected in customer research. Not enough suppliers understand how customers judge value for money in service, and how they react to changes in price. However, pricing research is not simple. Questions about willingness to pay produce misleading results, particularly in relation to services a respondent has never seen or used. Learning from customers' reaction to past price changes may be more effective.

PRICES AND COSTS

Changes in service policy should be analysed in terms of marginal or incremental (decremental) costs, rather than average costs. Incremental costs should then be related to incremental revenues, and finally to any consequent change in assets (e.g. changes in inventory, debt or credit levels). This produces a true marginal return on assets. But if all decisions were made on a marginal basis, a company might get in trouble with its overheads, as this approach implies no allocation of overhead. Discounting service because there is spare capacity in the service force today is dangerous. Overheads often grow with business activity, or just with time. An increase in activity generated by a price cut may generate more overhead, which the increased contribution does not cover.

Contribution margin

Because of this risk, some companies adopt a minimum contribution margin as a criterion for decisions, ensuring that there is no uncovered overhead. This can lead to non-market-related pricing if used as a pricing rule rather than to check the feasibility of a particular policy (e.g. a new service contract).

Which costs?

Service decisions should be based upon opportunity costs rather than financial costs. Opportunity costs take into account the value in use of the scarce resources. Using skilled engineers to service simple equipment wastes time which is more valuable than that of less skilled staff. If resources are not being used productively, opportunity costs are correspondingly low. If a policy is chosen because it uses underutilised resources, but if the resources are needed later, the original policy may need to be abandoned. In large businesses, it is normally a major exercise to find out the opportunity costs of a particular resource, let alone get management to accept the use of the concept. Hence the acceptance of accounting costs (whether historical or current) as the basis for most decisions.

PRICING STRATEGIES
Objectives

It is not always possible to separate pricing objectives from objectives for other service decisions, since price decisions are often taken in conjunction with them. The main objectives conventionally distinguished are:

Survival - to keep the service organisation just paying its way. This may involve reducing prices to just above marginal costs (to ensure some contribution).

Maximising current profits - rather than concentrating on longer term objectives. This objective may be adopted by a supplier exploiting a monopoly position (e.g. exclusive supplier of service to its own equipment, with no risk of competitive entry), or a company expecting to go out of business soon.

Leadership by share - to dominate the market by increasing volume, reducing costs, and making it difficult for smaller companies to remain viable.

Market leadership by quality - to establish a position as the premium supplier, supported by high quality service.

Pricing approaches

The approaches which may be used include:

Cost-plus pricing, where a constant mark-up on standard costs is used. This tends to ignore customer needs and competition. This method has advantages of simplicity and perceived equity. One point should be noted. Return on assets equals profit margin (mark-up) multiplied by asset turn. If the margin or the asset turn is too low, the business may not be viable.

Target profits / breakeven, where the margin is set to provide the right return on investment. If the market will not bear the price, the problem is not pricing, but the viability of the business. If fixed costs are high, too low a volume of business may mean a loss, while too high a volume (!) may produce high profits (when the company might have wanted a higher market share).

Perceived value pricing bases price on the value perceived by the customer. This depends on clearly establishing customer perceptions.

Going rate pricing is merely charging the going market price, typical of very competitive conditions, or when there is a strong price leader. This policy avoids conflict, and focuses management effort on reducing costs or on developing service products which are more differentiated and able to sustain a premium. It assumes that the service market has products which are standard enough for a going rate to be established and visible to customers.

Pricing to signal quality, where a premium product image cannot be sustained if it is cheap in absolute terms, irrespective of the size of the margin.

Variations on pricing approaches

There are a number of variations on pricing approaches, as follows:

Geographical pricing - varying prices to cover the costs of servicing different areas (e.g. via zone pricing). Whether geographical pricing can be sustained depends on the competitive situation amongst buyers and suppliers.

Discounting - for a variety of reasons, such as payment early or in cash, size of contract, contract renewal, or discrimination (according to buyer strength or need to obtain particular kinds of customer or segment business).

New product pricing - often designed to encourage trial for new kinds of service product, or to create a premium image for a particular contract.

Product line pricing - for consistency between prices of products in a range, or as an incentive to move to more profitable kinds of contract (trade-up). This includes co-ordination of equipment and service pricing, and parts and labour pricing. Competition and customer price-sensitivity are crucial here.

Most variations amount to using the principle of one pricing method to modify a price reached by another method (e.g. cost- plus pricing modified by perceived value pricing). Although this may seem messy, the real value of these approaches is their controllability and budgetability. Rules are established as to when variations are to be made.

Pricing and time

Service is often priced on a cost plus basis. For new equipment products, the mark-up may be small if the new product is very profitable in its own right. As the market develops and becomes more competitive, the margin that can be made on equipment sale may fall, and the supplier tries to take larger margins on service. This may tempt third party service to enter the market. If the equipment price is falling, customers may feel the relation between equipment and service prices has become distorted. Large customers may try to negotiate harder, and small customers search for other forms of service, or buy cheaper contracts. The result may be a ceiling on the proportionate relationship between maintenance contract price and machine price.

PRICING AND MARKET SEGMENTATION

Margin pressure may be partly avoided by use of market segmentation. A high price contract may be marketed to users needing high quality service, even if the costs of providing it do not rise in proportion to quality. The ability to segment often increases as the user base becomes larger and more varied, but

134

demands high quality information on customers' level of service needs, together with applying marketing techniques to service.

Price sensitivity

Suppliers often assume their customers are highly price sensitive. But in some sectors, surveys show that factors like level of support and administrative relationship are more important than price. Price-sensitive customers may be used as a stick to "beat" the finance department in requesting lower prices. Customers may compare prices as part of a negotiating strategy, with no intention of switching on price grounds. The costs or risks of switching may be too high. The answer to the challenge "the price is too high" is usually "develop your business such that your customers become less price sensitive".

The problem of large customers

Smaller suppliers who find that their top two or three customers account for 30-40% of their business may be frightened at the thought of losing their business, and discount if these customers start to exercise their negotiating strength. This applies particularly to some third party maintenance companies. The solution is to try to avoid this position, by developing a customer mix strategy. This requires:
- Deciding what your strengths are (company, products, service).
- Targeting activities on those customers where your added value is highest and where your ability to get the customer locked in is greatest.
- Preparing contingencies if certain business is lost, and reducing cost exposure in the case of loss (i.e. not letting expenses run too far ahead, but holding them to where they would be if revenue were lower).

Segmenting by responsiveness

Some buyers are not very conscious of the price they are paying for service, of competitors' prices, or of the full benefits of using one or other service product. The customer may not be as well informed as the supplier, or care as much about choice between companies or products. Lack of price awareness may be due to complexity of pricing (e.g. where service is included in the sale price) or outdating of price information. Lack of price awareness is a good basis for price discrimination (depending on competitive conditions).

Different pricing rules in different situations

Customers may be more aware of or sensitive to some elements of price than others. They may be more aware of initial purchase price than subsequent charges for maintenance or spares. Suppliers lose opportunities of increasing prices on certain items in the range by pricing each product by the same rules. Capitalising in all opportunities for gaining high prices in situations of less sensitivity to price compensates for having to reduce margins on products where there is no avoiding head-on price competition.

Customer pricing

The same principle applies to pricing for individual customers. The first step is to ensure that the costs of servicing particular customers or groups of customers (to make the analysis more manageable) are known. You may want to look at the costs of and profits from servicing groups of customers responsible for more than a certain proportion of company revenue/profit. The groups should be chosen according to the company's field structure, as cost information is more likely to be available in this way. If the structure is geographical, this means looking at the costs of service in particular areas. If costs are averaged over all customers, then some business will be unprofitable, while potentially profitable business may be lost.

If the costs of servicing a particular customer are known, then some may be chargeable to that customer, particularly if he is less sensitive to charges for items where he can see a logic for a premium charge. Examples include communication and customisation. One strategy is to gain a position in new customers by a low price, and then add charges as the relationship develops. Ideally (but not always), the charges correspond to real additional, higher-margin, services. The diagnosis of the need for these services will often only be possible once a commercial relationship exists with the customer.

MARKETING SERVICE

Suppliers who do not market service may find their service is a commodity, with nothing to differentiate it from that of other suppliers. Service management may be coerced by marketing into reducing the price of service for fear of losing equipment sales. In certain circumstances this may be right, but it should be monitored - it may be a sign that marketing has failed to differentiate equipment products as well! If a reduction is necessary (either in list price or via discounts), it should be deducted from the sales budget.

If service is well marketed, discounting can be minimised. This means creating an image which will justify a premium. Some service managers initiate campaigns to boost the image of service, while overall company image is weak (e.g. because marketing concentrates on selling products, not the company). Such campaigns should be part of a co-ordinated company image campaign. The perception of quality of service is as important as the actual service. This perception is created not just through promotion, but also through the service force, managers, call receivers, and administrative staff. The attitude of service force and managers must be consistent with the premium. Creating a premium image of service may require upgrading it in relation to sales. If service is a second class citizen, the image is hard to sustain.

Sustaining a premium

Usually, the leading two or three suppliers in a sector can sustain a premium over others. This is a consequence of how suppliers come to be leaders. Leadership comes from long term efforts to build customer loyalty, by creating perceived and actual strengths which other suppliers do not have. These may relate to equipment, supplier or service. Suppliers who are known to look after customers are hard to displace with low priced service. Customers are reluctant to save a few percent by breaking a smooth relationship. Suppliers who sell just on price tend to be easier to displace, if matched on price.

The competitive situation

In a crowded market place, where all suppliers are trying to gain or defend market share, sustaining a premium depends on developing a strong image with existing and prospective customers. The less competitive the market and the less concentrated the buying power, the weaker the link between prices and costs and the greater the opportunities for making profit by discriminating between customers with differing price sensitivities.

Barriers to market entry

One obstacle to full-profit pricing is weakness of barriers to entry. Weak barriers may cause prices to be set below highest profitability levels to deter entry. The level depends on the commitment that needs to be made by other service suppliers to enter the market. This commitment is not just for "hard" investments, such as engineer recruitment and training or spare parts inventory, but also the marketing effort required to break customer loyalty.

One way companies break into a market is to pick segments or customers likely to respond, rather than a broad front attack. Prior action (identification of customers who think their level of service is deteriorating, and remedying the situation) may forestall entry relatively cheaply. If financial constraints hamper an overall solution, it may be wise to discriminate in favour of dissatisfied customers (on service or, as a last resort, on price), funding the required costs from revenue from more satisfied customers. Some suppliers are noted for their ability to discriminate between customers on this basis (derived from in-depth knowledge of the customer and flexible enough pricing procedures). It goes without saying that the lower the service cost base, the more freedom there is to engage in defensive and offensive strategies.

Invoicing problems
Pricing variations and flexibility may be needed to:
- Maximise price discrimination between customers.
- Tighten control over customers.
- Capitalise on shorter-term opportunities.

This can produce complex pricing structures, raising levels of invoice queries and administrative costs. This is more likely if invoicing is carried out centrally. Problems may be reduced by invoicing from the sales branch. The need for dedicated invoicing staff can usually be avoided by using clerical staff for support as well as invoicing. Prevention is better than cure. Suppliers who anticipate this problem develop discounting procedures for implementation at local level, controlled tightly through a discount budget. The basic pricing structure is kept simple in this way.

CHECKLIST FOR CHAPTER 7

Service products

* Is there a clear role for service product policy in our service plan?
* Is packaging of service into products treated as a key service decision?
* Are our overall service objectives as clearly stated as they need to be for service product policy decisions to be made?
* Have we understood the role of service product policy in improving customer satisfaction?
* Do we have a robust process for generating service product ideas, researching the demand for them, evaluating them, choosing between them, testing them, and marketing them?
* Do the techniques we use for evaluating different service product ideas take into account our strategic and financial needs and objectives, and our resource constraints?
* Do we consider the full range of service product options that are available?
* Does our service market information system routinely yield information which would show whether our service product policy needed changing?
* Do we use market segmentation approaches for establishing whether there are opportunities for improving our achievement of service objectives by designing or modifying particular service products for the needs of particular market segments or customers?
* Have we considered test marketing new service products?

Service prices

* Does our service market information system yield information about the sensitivity of customers to different service price levels?
* Are the costs of supplying service via different products, to different areas, customers, equipment, and so on, known and documented?
* Are our service pricing objectives clearly stated in our service plan?
* Do we consider the full range of pricing approaches and variations that are available (e.g. cost-plus, target profits, break-even, perceived value, going-rate, quality signal, geographic, discounting, new product, product line)?
* Does the choice we make between different pricing approaches bear a clear relation to our service objectives and our competitive position?
* Do we use service pricing to erect and maintain barriers to market and customer entry by competitors, as appropriate?

* Do we use market segmentation approaches to establish whether there are opportunities for obtaining higher prices for particular service products in certain market segments or with certain customers?
* Do we know where our strengths as a service organisation lie, in which situations we deliver highest added value, and therefore where we are most likely to be able to achieve a premium price or to resist over-discounting?
* Is the way in which we market service (and indeed the whole company) conducive to justifying the prices that we charge or wish to charge?
* Do we have a customer pricing facility (e.g. for major customers)?
* Do we ensure that service pricing decisions take into account the need for ease of invoicing?

8 OPERATING METHODS

Here, we begin our analysis of the process by which service is delivered. A key element of this process is what happens when a customer calls to report a fault. Managing this element is central to the efficiency and profitability of service. It also plays a vital role in creating customer satisfaction. By starting with the element of the service process that is responsible for dealing with the customer, we are making the important point that the system must be customer-oriented, although our key objective may be profit. The system for delivering service to the customer must be technically sound, rapid enough to deliver required response times, responsive to the broader determinants of customer satisfaction, and capable of being used by the kind of staff likely to be in charge of day to day operations.

The key staff in daily control of operations at the customer interface are:
- Service managers.
- Supervisors.
- Call receivers.
- Work controllers.
- Stock controllers.

They work at the interface between customers and overall company targets, such as profit, cost containment, revenue, response times, uptime, or customer satisfaction ratings. How these overall targets are allocated as individual targets depends on the overall structure and system of responsibilities of the operation (see Chapter 13), and also on the particular needs of those customers for whom each part of the service organisation is responsible.

WORK CONTROL

The work controller makes an important contribution to achieving engineer efficiency and to delivering service to meet customer needs. Work planning can achieve considerable savings, whether in travel or in inventory carried by the engineer. It may also enable a supplier to operate with engineers of different skill levels, according to the mix of equipment in a particular area. In planning engineer workloads, the aims of work control should be to:

- Achieve the maximum level of customer satisfaction consistent with resource-oriented objectives of the service organisation (e.g. profit).
- Ensure that breakdowns are visited and dealt with within the target committed to customers (e.g. response time, uptime).
- Provide engineers with a continuity of jobs.
- Minimise engineer travel.
- Ensure that engineers with the correct skills attend calls.
- Provide the engineer with as rational a structuring of his day's work as is consistent with other constraints, to maximise employee motivation.
- Arrange spares support when necessary

Basic requirements

The work controller should have a good knowledge of the geography of his area, if engineer travel is to be minimised and the best service provided. The work controller needs a map showing customer locations, and also areas where travel is difficult or easy (including variations by time of day , week or even year). This helps in deciding which engineer to send. The work controller usually needs to be in contact with engineers during the day, to give spares back-up if the engineer's parts kit does not include needed spares, and so that on finishing each job, the controller can advise the engineer of new jobs or alteration to priorities, and monitor the time taken to complete the job.

Planning ahead

The work controller should plan engineer workload as far ahead as possible. If average response times are the same length as the sum of average repair and travel times, planning is difficult. The next destination of the engineer may only become clear during his current call. The further ahead the work is planned, the easier it is to include work such as planned maintenance and (if used) customer care calls.

The work controller's role

In many companies, work controller and call receiver roles are merged. This eases communication between customer, company and engineer concerning the nature of the service required. Alternatively, call receivers may have some technical expertise, passing their analysis of the fault to the work controller, who sends the appropriate engineer. Some companies have separate locations for call receipt and work control, typically central call receipt and local work control. Unless this produces great staff savings, resulting communication problems may reduce efficiency and customer satisfaction.

CALL RECEIPT

Call receipt may be located locally, regionally or even nationally. Location of call receipt in local branches may give the customer the feeling that he is receiving more personal attention. However, centralised organisation may provide cost savings, because:

- Fewer call receivers are required.
- Call receivers can be better trained.
- Technical back-up is available.
- There may be better control over response times.

The disadvantages of central organisation are:

- Customers may have to telephone long distance.
- Customers are likely to get a different call receiver each time.
- Call receivers are unlikely to know the customer or his equipment.

These disadvantages can be minimised by good organisation, good training, and on-line data bases carrying customer and equipment details.

Diagnosis

In many companies, call receivers (whether local or not) simply accept the call and send an engineer. For some types of equipment, the number of calls can be reduced if the nature of the fault can be established over the telephone and the customer instructed how to deal with it. If a call is necessary, such procedures enable engineers to take unusual parts if the fault requires them. Remote diagnosis (see Chapter 4) is increasingly being used to support this process (and eventually eliminate calls), while expert systems are used to diagnose the causes of faults on very expensive equipment. Three main approaches exist for analysing incoming breakdown calls. They are:

- Call receiver with standard questionnaire.
- Manager deals with customer breakdown calls.
- Technical expertise is on tap to investigate the problem over the phone.

Some companies take the view that customers do not have the interest or expertise to answer detailed questions by telephone. This applies particularly if the equipment is operated mainly by occasional users. Some vetting of breakdown reports is desirable, as engineers may travel long distances for trivial jobs. Correct diagnosis of the cause of failure may avoid such calls, or identify what spares are likely to be needed.

Filter procedures

Some companies (typically larger ones) avoid using technically qualified staff on call receipt and use a filter procedure by which the breakdown can be diagnosed as a simple problem or as requiring particular expertise to resolve it. The call is then handed to the appropriate expert for further diagnosis.

Informal prior calls

Whatever the formal system, it is common (and good) practice for engineers to ring customers to discuss the problem. This has the advantage of the personal touch, and may enable a call to be avoided. The engineer may have the authority to reschedule non- urgent calls. Where engineers work in small teams, the senior engineer is in a good position to assess which engineer to send, taking into account personality, location and workload. More appropriate spare parts may also be taken.

Engineer involvement

Difficulties may arise because an engineer becomes involved with favourite customers and gives them preferential service. With the call receiver as the liaison contact, this is less likely to happen.

Call planning

How calls are handled by work control depends on the objectives of the service operation. These objectives may be broken down into detailed rules, relating to the following kinds of factor:
  - Fastest presence on site.
  - Shortest on-site time.
  - Best solution for customer satisfaction.
  - Minimum operating costs.
  - Specific engineer to attend.
  - Specialist to respond.

Call prioritisation

If one engineer handles all the calls in an area, work control's only task is call prioritisation. Where several engineers of a given skill level are responsible for an area, and where an expert might be required, work control uses a complex set of rules for call allocation, often via a computerised allocation procedure (perhaps based on mathematical programming techniques). Such procedures use judgmental assignment and filtering rules, which contain elements relating to the importance to the company of particular customers (or types of customer), or of achieving particular response times versus repair times, as well as data on expected call duration, and so forth. The use of such procedures is limited by the data available at the time of call receipt.

These procedures can be visualised as treating customers who call as if they are in competition for scarce service resources. Because calls do not come in simultaneously, but throughout the day, the situation is one of queue formation, and therefore amenable to treatment by queuing theory. This does not assume that customers have to be dealt with in the order in which they call, but does require some mechanism for prioritising customers. This means deciding on criteria for prioritising, and on the relative importance of particular criteria. These may be handled by factor weighting techniques. For example, attributes of a call can be given weights according to their judged relative importance. These weights might relate to type of equipment, nature of fault reported or status of customer. A priority factor in the queue can then be allocated on the basis of the sum of the weighted factors. Absolute criteria may also be used (e.g. particular customers, equipment or faults take priority over all others). This is equivalent to giving a particular variable a very high weighting in a factor weighting approach).

The system can be designed to provide options to the work controller. So, it might give the option of an engineer unfamiliar with the customer to call within four hours, or an engineer who knows the customer to call within six hours. If the customer is thought to prefer a regular engineer, but it is not known by how much, the choice could even be passed to the customer.

A SCHEMATIC WORK CONTROL PROGRAMME
To design a work control programme, we need to construct a set of questions and filters which the programme would use, if the data were available, and

then reduce this set according to company requirements and data availability. Here is an example. Note that the ordering of the filters can be switched according to different priorities. Comments are added in parentheses.

Step 1
Call is received and time noted.

Step 2
Customer is identified; e.g.
- For which customer
- For which category of customer.

(We need to identify the location of the customer and possibly the importance of that customer to us, not only in terms of service profit from the equipment in question, but for all his equipment, and ideally profit arising or likely to arise from sales. In practice, the latter information is unlikely to be available, unless the sales department has created a priority category of customer - e.g. one with whom sales negotiations are currently taking place. This process may result in a customer being given a particular priority. This information will also be used to establish whether we need to use an engineer with particular familiarity with this customer's needs.)

Step 3
Nature of fault is established; e.g.
- To which equipment.
- When it occurred.
- Why it occurred.
- Under what conditions.

(This helps identify what parts and engineer skills may be required. This may be a two-stage step, with reference back to a technical expert.)

Step 4
Customer dependence established; e.g.
- Does customer have alternative equipment?
- What are costs to customer of delay?

(The company may prioritise calls by degree of customer urgency. Some companies give customers the right to say whether a call is urgent. This 'trust' system may work well - customers know that it fails if abused. Customers may be allowed a given number of high-priority call 'rights'. A company which knows its customers very well may handle the need for prioritisation via understanding and negotiation rather than formal systems.)

Step 5
Likely repair need identified;
- Length of time to repair.
- Parts required.

(This is an internal calculation, which requires reference to equipment history and spare parts usage data.)

Step 6
Available staff identified;
- Staff of expected required skill level identified.
- Location checked.
- Availability estimated.

(The feasibility of using this data when the call arrives depends on the nature of communication between engineer and office. With advanced local communications systems available, this data can be computerised.)

Step 7
Parts provision;
- Expected needed parts availability checked.
- Provision arranged.

(This requires reference to inventory data, including that on parts carried by engineers - including kit depletion data.)

Step 8
Engineer assigned;
(This is where the prioritisation rules referred to above may be applied. This could be a deferred decision.)

Step 9
Engineer contacted and informed.

Step 10
Customer informed.

Step 11

Engineer contacts customer.

(This is an optional step, but may improve customer care and diagnosis of problem. The call may be fed back into the system at this point if significant new information is obtained.)

WORK CONTROL RESPONSIBILITY

Whether or not work control is computerised, most companies give the task of call allocation to staff with a reasonable level of responsibility. They may be specialist work controllers, or other staff. The choice depends upon:

- Resource availability.
- Relative strengths associated with each function.
- Type of individual in each function.

The general advantages of each choice are as follows:

Call receiver

The call receiver is often the first and sometimes focal point of contact between customer and supplier. This means that it is feasible to concentrate background information on customer, equipment history, and contract type at this point. Assuming enough stability in the organisation and not too many customers to be dealt with, the call receiver's knowledge may be a major strength in dealing with customers.

Specialist work controller

Specialist work controllers may have much better control over information on engineer availability, enabling better forward planning. This is especially so in an office with a high frequency of incoming calls, where a call receiver or service manager may not have time to keep close tabs on engineer availability.

Local manager

Local managers, by virtue of seniority and (normally) experience, should have a more balanced appreciation of customer service and technical implications. Given appropriate flexibility in targets, this may allow better adjustment of service requirements to customer needs, taking into account the long term view. However, too great an involvement of the manager in call allocation may impair his capacity to manage the overall operation.

Senior engineer

The senior engineer has many of the advantages of the service manager, and may be superior in local and site knowledge and attention to customer care. As a senior engineer working with a team, he may know the individuals' strengths and weaknesses, and be able to deploy his team more effectively. However, he may not have the degree of latitude possessed by the service manager.

Local engineer

Engineers may have deeper knowledge than senior engineers of certain customers or of particular equipment and its faults. They may also have very high personal motivation. These factors may prevent them taking the overall view.

CONTROL OF REPAIRABLE MODULES

So far, we have concentrated on control of the manpower element of service. Another major element of cost over which the service manager has some control is parts. The management element of this control is most important in handling of repairable modules. Though off-site module repair may provide better customer service, reduced costs and increased quality of repair, control of module return and repair is often difficult.

The repair centre has limited capacity, the demand for which may sometimes be exceeded due to high random fluctuations in module failure, possibly delaying repairs (unless these are contracted-out). This may be avoided by keeping a stock of modules, an expensive solution, as modules are usually costly, absorbing cashflow and eventually having to be written off. Through tight control this investment can be minimised and availability of modules improved.

Applying inventory control

After manufacture or purchase, a module starts at central stores, is moved to local stores, to the engineer kit and fitted to the equipment. The replaced module is returned by the engineer via the local stores to the repair centre, repaired and modified as necessary, then returned to the central stores. Reticence by engineers to return modules reduces availability. This requires careful control to prevent excess inventory. The inventory control system should be able to highlight where modules are and how long they have been there. It is

149

rarely necessary for engineers to hold used modules for more than a day or two. The local branch can also turn them round in a similar time.

The number of modules held at each place should be determined by the principles of stock cover (Chapter 9), taking into account supply time or (for repairables) the interval between despatch and return. A module exchange procedure is required at central stores, to cushion field service against the time taken to repair modules. This principle should be used with engineers to ensure no personal stocks are built up and used ones are returned immediately. If inventory at local level is also determined by stock cover needs, then the only other stock will be either awaiting repair or located in central stores.

The number of modules required to balance the workload of the repair centre can be calculated from fluctuations in the rate at which they are received for repair. The higher the proportion of repairs done by the centre, the less stock is required. This leaves the major stockholding at the central stores, unless one of the more advanced integrated stock control systems is in use.

Loading the repair centre

Efficient supply of repairable parts depends on obtaining the right level of availability from the repair centre. We have to answer two questions:
- Which modules need repairing?
- What is repair priority?

Some modules returned from the field do not need repairing, because:
1. The cost of repair is potentially too high.
2. The item has been superceded.
3. There is no shortage of working modules.

The logging-in system at the repair centre should identify these categories. The identification of category 3 for declining products or obsolescent modules can reduce the repair centre queue significantly. These modules can be removed for disposal or stored unrepaired. Repair of the rest may be contracted to other parts of the company, equipment suppliers or local specialists.These activities should be controlled by the repair centre. Local companies used for repairs must be assessed for the speed and variability of timing of module return as well as for technical competence. Local repairers can provide more flexible repair capacity. Where repair is not practical, the decision to scrap should be made swiftly so that replacements can be ordered if justified. Repair priorities can normally be set by the availability of good modules and usage rates. If resource constraints mean that modules are being repaired for particular customers, prioritisation between customers may be required.

MONITORING SYSTEMS

Communication is a vital element in the system. Information is generated in one area and then assembled in various ways to provide information for other areas. So, the engineer visit report that identifies a fault can be used for:

- Charging the customer.
- Diagnosing similar faults in future.
- Repair statistics.
- Redesign of faulty components.

The areas most dependent on information from engineers are:

- Line management performance monitoring.
- Financial controls.
- Design and development.
- Stock replenishment.
- Repair centre.
- Inventory management and logistics.

The systems for these areas should be integrated to avoid duplication. In many companies layers of systems exist to close gaps in the original system. This results in information being recorded at various levels of detail for each system. The effectiveness of information flows should be checked as follows:

1. List the information gathered within the service organisation.
2. Determine who uses it and for what - what changes are made as a result of it, and whether they help direct the company towards its targets.
3. Identify and remove redundant reporting (e.g. if information intended as control information, but no controls use it).
4. Determine who provides the information.
5. Find out what feedback there is to the originator of the information to enable him to see that the effort on recording is worthwhile.
6. Note items of information which are recorded more than once, and change systems to remove double reporting.

7. Identify needed control or management information needed which is absent.

Recording methods

The methods used by companies to record their service data vary widely. Most have engineer worksheets for each job. These are normally filled in by engineers on site, although some data is available to the work controller and can be reported from the centre. Some companies use more sophisticated methods, including direct entry into portable terminals, and bar-codes and scanners to record equipment being serviced and parts usage. The costs of such approaches are falling quickly, while their reliability is increasing. Improved communications facilities are also helping.

Benefits of automation

The benefits of such approaches are reduced paperwork by engineer and clerical staff and increased accuracy in recording. Speed of entry into central records may be increased if the portable terminal includes a modem, so that service details can be transmitted directly after completion of the service. This can reduce the lag in tracking spares usage. Local stock replacement can be triggered directly after service. If this is linked with parts reordering, the level of stock in local stores can be cut. Automation of reporting provides management with more rapid up-dating on the current situation, enabling quicker response to problems. For service on a time and materials basis which is billed centrally, the cash flow benefits may be significant.

Integrated systems

Financial information generally takes longer than operating information to arrive at headquarters, except in those companies with integrated systems. In some cases service branches get no analysis of their full costs and profits. Computerised systems are now available for companies covering the control and reporting of field service. These provide operating and financial information at local and national level. Many such systems have been developed by companies for their own use. In general they provide good but not complete coverage of financial and operating information.

152

Integrated systems yield great benefits. Managers can see the deployment of the engineer force and modify operations of their group as priorities change. They have a wide range of information available immediately on which to base their decisions and can monitor the effectiveness of their actions, as well as carrying out simulations. The increase in speed at which information is available and acted upon raises the potential for good management and improved results. The flexibility of targets and the analysis of information by various 'cuts' shows what targets are possible. Such systems can be extended to cover a wide range of associated areas, such as:

- Spare parts stockholding (centrally and in other local stores).
- Machine population changes (current and forecast).
- Breakdown statistics (for parts and subassemblies).

Simple stock monitoring systems may be included in integrated service systems. Storage may be provided for large amounts of unanalysed breakdown report data, for possible future analyses. Some systems include tracking of repairable modules through repair. It is difficult to include capacity plans and load forecasting in such systems, though tracking of trends is often included. Few systems deal with call priorities, optimising travel distances, call organisation, or engineer team composition, all areas which can result in considerable improvements in costs and customer satisfaction.

Use of records

If records are used negatively (e.g. to pressure engineers into meeting shorter service time targets, without analysis of the nature of calls), poor reporting may result. So, reports should monitor the key targets together with major problems. The computerised systems used in some companies only monitor performance against target, not reasons for deviation. The usual channel for the latter is the management meeting.

Controlling engineer time

One problem in controlling engineer time allocation is that monitoring is done by the engineer himself. The engineer may record it according to what seems to him to indicate efficient working. Travel or job time may increase when there is no pressure. The results may look good on paper, but some time might be better employed. The measurement of engineer waiting time may not be too accurate.

Real engineer activity may only be established if relative performance monitoring is introduced to check slack time.

CHECKLIST FOR CHAPTER 8

Work control
* Are the objectives of work control clearly specified? Do they include reference to customer satisfaction, as well as resource optimisation?
* Does the way in which work control responsibility has been allocated (to call receivers, specialist work controllers, local managers, senior engineers, or engineers themselves) exploit fully the particular skills, knowledge and motivation of the staff concerned, without impeding the efficiency of the service organisation or the achievement of customer satisfaction?
* Are response times flexible enough (given customer needs) to maximise opportunities for forward planning of calls, thereby optimising exploitation of engineer time?
* If a queue of calls builds up, do we have a robust system for prioritising calls? Are we using computerised procedures for applying prioritisation rules? Do the rules we use tie closely to the needs of customers and the importance of particular customers to us?
* If call handling is separated from work control, do call handlers obtain all the information that work controllers need to prioritise calls and allocate engineers so as to optimise achievement of company objectives?
* Do we encourage engineers or supervisors to call customers informally to check on the reasons for failure, and (in the case of supervisors) to allocate the most suitable engineer for the job?

Repairable module control
* Are we applying all the principles of inventory control (particularly stock cover) to repairable modules?
* Do we have clear rules for deciding which modules should be repaired, and in what order of priority? Does our logging-in system for modules identify which priority category a module belongs to?

Monitoring systems
* Is all the information that is gathered within the service organisation used (directly or indirectly) for improving service performance?
* Do we occasionally check our reporting system for redundancy or double reporting of information?

* Is feedback given to providers of information as to its purpose?
* Have we understood all the benefits of automation in reporting (e.g. manpower and spares resourcing, improved customer satisfaction)?
* Are we optimising exploitation of automation in reporting systems?
* Is financial information reported and transmitted early enough for management to take action on it?
* Do our systems track all causes of breakdown?
* Do our systems cover call prioritisation and optimisation of travel costs?
* Does our monitoring concentrate on key targets, major problems and the reasons for their occurrence, to ensure focus on constructive ways of improving performance, rather than general pressure on engineers?
* Are we sure that information being recorded by the engineer is not modified by engineers to accord with what they think management would like to hear?

9 INVENTORY MANAGEMENT AND CONTROL

SPARES AVAILABILITY

Many companies spend a high proportion of their service revenue on spare parts, the proportion depending on product repairability, service policy and inventory organisation. Many companies are tightening their controls on logistic support, against a background of complex and changing service requirements, relating to factors such as:

- Medium and low value parts.
- Wide distribution of usage points.
- Immediate requirement for parts.
- Low usage rates.
- High service level required.
- Wider equipment mix.

Many suppliers traditionally allowed spares stocks to build up to cover any contingency, but are now taking a much more professional approach, because service needs are making existing stock targets more difficult to reach.

Spares service targets

Failure to maintain sufficient control over spare parts inventory can lead to reduced service levels due to stock-outs on some parts, together with high stock levels on other parts. Attempts to achieve adequate service levels without appropriate control normally leads to inflated inventories and excess costs. Better organised companies are now balancing inventory targets via:

- Engineer kit or local kit design.
- Defined service policies, stocking levels and locations for each part.
- Wide visibility of stock levels, due to improved communication systems.

Service levels

The stock level at each location should be governed by supply lead times and required service levels. Most companies exercise tight control over national stocks, from which there is usually a high service level. At local stores, the service level is usually lower, with a narrower range of parts being carried.

Engineer kits contain a limited parts range. If the engineer returns to base between calls, he can pick up spares for the next call. Items used can be replaced and the kit optimised for the next call. If returning to base for parts costs much more (due to extra travel time and its consequences for level of service) than proceeding direct to the next call, this may outweigh parts inventory savings. The engineer kit needs to be more comprehensive, to cover a wider range of likely faults. This is easier to implement if target response times are long enough to allow call planning. Otherwise, only a general parts kit can be carried, which may lead to more split calls to collect parts. This can be avoided by engineer specialisation, which has its own costs.

Service response times also affect stock policies at local and national level. Most companies' response times are much shorter than parts supply times to the local stores. Especially with less frequently used items, the cost of holding them in all local areas is very high. They may have to be held centrally, ready for rapid despatch. For some suppliers, lead times for supply to local centres are falling towards call response times (which may be rising). The stores organisation may become a logistic support operation. The only stock held locally will be high usage parts. All other items can be returned to central stores. Central stores must supply parts fast and reliably. Distribution costs have to be monitored to ensure that this change is cost effective. This change can save up to 30% of current stock value, plus much of the cost of writing off obsolete items. Inventory costs are reduced by slower service response times, better communications between stores, faster supply lead times and greater consistency in repair methods. A regional service policy can also help to minimise the inventory. If high service levels are concentrated in regions of high equipment density, stock may also be lower.

STOCK BALANCE
Stock control effectiveness is a function of customer service provided and stock held to support it. The amount of stock needed depends upon expected demand. The formula for measuring months of stock cover is :-

$$\text{Stock cover} = \frac{\text{Current stock}}{\text{Annual usage}} \times 12, \quad \text{where stock and usage are normally measured in value terms}$$

The reciprocal definition (stock-turn) may be used, but since it has less physical meaning, most companies prefer the stock cover measure.

Improved equipment reliability combined with the need to hold a minimum stock leads to a gradual increase in spares stock cover for spares. This may make it more difficult to decide how many items to hold to provide acceptable service level to engineers while avoiding excess stocks. Even companies with good control systems have a large amount of slow moving stock.

Repairable items

For suppliers with a high proportion of repairable items, the situation is even more complex. Financial figures, actual usage and stock quantities must be used (particularly for high value items) to identify opportunities for savings. Actual usage is measured by the items used to repair equipment (i.e. not by items used to repair modules which are then held in stock). The stock is taken as the total number of items in the repair cycle, including defective items being returned and items at the repair centre. The total months of cover should be higher for repairable items, to cover the return and repair time.

Measuring usage is complicated by the practice of using modules as test devices. A module is often tried in equipment and then returned to the kit because it did not rectify the fault. This trial fix is not counted as a 'use'. If the module is left in the machine and the one from the equipment returned in the kit, a judgement has to be made about the returned module's quality. If it is considered satisfactory, the event does not count as usage. If the module is sent back and repaired, the replacement counts as usage.

Stocks of parts may be kept on customer site, if the customer can make simple module replacement himself. The module is then replaced by the customer sending it in for exchange. To exploit this possibility, equipment must be designed to make replacement very simple.

Total national stocks and supply

The stock held within national operations depends largely on the quality of supply from the parts source to the national parts operation. There is often some lack of trust between parts supplier and stock control. Even where the source is within the company, there is little pooling of expertise in technical, logistic and financial matters. This leads to:

- Over-specification of parts requirement by international technical specialists.
- Rejection of their advice in national operations.
- National management re-defining kit content.
- Patchy demand patterns, leading to high stocks.
- Many companies carrying out special stock write-off projects.

How to improve stock balance

Stock balance can be improved in many ways. One is via integration of stocks at local store and engineer level (e.g. via 'swap kits'). Another way is to treat all stock in the company as one stock in distributed warehouses. This can result in abandoning either central or local stores. Even if the national warehouse is abolished, it is important to maintain central control over the stock, to maintain co-ordination of supply with true usage. This solution is more suitable for companies with fairly standard local operations. Where local and engineer stocks are very varied, a significant proportion of the whole spare parts inventory may still need to be carried at national level.

End of life

Product lifetime depends on commercial or technical usefulness. Changes to equipment design, followed by field modification programmes, render some parts obsolete at a stroke. However, obsolete machines have to be supported long after production has ceased, necessitating small batch production and increasing parts costs. This problem may be aggravated by the change from electro- mechanical to electronic technology.

It rarely pays to buy the all-time requirement of parts in one order, except where there are immense economies in order size, or where availability may cease. In such cases, an estimate of total forward usage is needed. This means estimating the phase-out rate of the equipment and the future failure rate of the components. Near the end of the technical life of a product, when the machine population is usually small, these factors are difficult to determine. If we allow too great a margin for error, there will be a large stock write-off when the equipment is completely terminated.

Most suppliers have a separate control for spare parts on product launch and for the support of mature equipment. At the other end of the product support cycle, identification of when to reduce spares provisioning is often poor. Excess stocks result if a company enters the obsolescence phase without realising it. As demand diminishes, stock becomes more difficult to balance. The problem of excess stock from this cause is best avoided by changing the control procedure between supply and obsolescence phases.

LOCAL STORES

Local stores are generally the responsibility of stores controllers, whose prime function is to control issue and receipt of stock. They are not well trained to evaluate optimum stock levels and balance inventory. In the view of most local service managers, customer service takes priority over stock considerations. This can lead to inventory problems such as:

- Allowing engineers to carry excessive parts.
- Access to stores for everyone.
- Over stocking.
- Slow return of repairable items.
- Proliferation of item types held.

The more local stores there are, the more stock will be needed, but the better the level of service. In theory, the safety stock level increases as the square root of the number of stores. In practice, the increase may be greater, particularly for items where the safety level is low in absolute terms. If the safety stock is calculated as 5, stores will hold 5 in addition to batch or delivery quantities. If the safety stock is 0.5, stores will hold 1. Some suppliers hold all parts for which there is any potential usage, leading to stores full of non-moving parts. This is not a good solution. It is more effective to rationalise stockholding by dividing inventory between national and local stocks, holding high value, slow moving or physically large items at national level, backed by rapid despatch to the engineer or local stores, and other parts at local level.

Effectiveness within the stores

Within the parts store, effectiveness is likely to be achieved by having:

- An enclosed stores area.
- A member of staff with overall authority for stores.

161

- Accurate stock recording procedures.
- Stock level recording systems.

ENGINEER KITS

The engineer may be provided with spares via a personal general spares kit or a special kit for the equipment being serviced. The general kit is appropriate where the engineer carries out a number of calls on a narrow range of equipment without returning to base. The special kit provides a better level of spares availability for the specific job, but the engineer must be provided with different kits for different jobs. Kits are particularly suitable where there is accurate forward planning of engineer workload and where the engineer is servicing a wide product range.

A kit can be provided to the engineer as a set of parts which he replenishes as required, or as a swap kit, which the storeman exchanges for a complete one, identifies parts which have been used, replaces them and reissues the kit later. The swap kit has advantages in control of parts and accuracy of records, as stock is all stores stock until used, not engineer stock. It is especially useful if the company can carry a series of kits for each type of product or module. These can be spread more thinly between engineers than if engineers had their own stocks, improving parts availability and reducing stocks. Repairable parts are also returned more quickly. The best solution may be a regional kit policy. Areas of low machine density need engineer kits, or else they suffer long response times. Areas of high machine density have dedicated product engineers or swap kits. Current trends suggest that swap kits will dramatically improve the quality of engineer kit information.

MONITORING SYSTEMS

For some companies, the development of computerised stock recording systems is more important than engineer activity recording, given the serious effects of lack of parts on customer service. The control of central stock levels is fairly tight in most companies, but there are less strict controls on local and engineer levels. Many companies, particularly larger ones, are developing local systems. Smaller companies have less formal systems at these levels. This results in higher inventories for equivalent operating conditions.

The control of supply may be through individual orders or scheduling. Parts provision from national inventory is usually carried out by orders from local stores. This may not be optimal in stock balance terms, but it ensures reasonable parts availability at local stores. Some companies already run integrated processes, with regional and central stores controlled (centrally) on one system. Others allow regional responsibility for local inventory holding and include the costs in regional profit assessments. In some companies, engineer kits are included in the system. In general, stocks are best organised at national level (preventing inflated stock-to-stock transactions), combining required service levels with the usual principles of inventory and purchasing management (e.g. economic order quantities). National control gives more scope for optimising physical distribution methods, often a weak point, as many companies do not control parts distribution costs closely enough.

In theory, the level of service required from local stock can be calculated from the expected breakdown frequency of the various types of equipment being supported. This may have to be adjusted for the criticality of certain parts or equipment (e.g. if particular important customers are so dependent on a certain piece of equipment that they should never have to wait for spares). In practice, companies rarely use theoretical stock control methods at local level. Stock is assessed through a combination of experience, mean time between failure, and failure of similar parts.

STOCK MANAGEMENT
Many companies are currently very concerned about the size of their investment in stock and the availability of spares. This has caused them to re-examine their management structure and responsibilities in order to improve spares and logistic support. The main areas for improvement are usually:
- Control over local stocks (ideally through integrated systems).
- Better stock balance at all levels.
- Improved field policies (and improved communication of these policies).
- Better information from the marketing function on likely equipment populations.

CHECKLIST FOR CHAPTER 9

* Do we achieve the right balance between control of spare parts inventory and service to the customer?
* Does engineer kit composition match likely travel and fault patterns?
* Do our systems provide the data to enable us to optimise kits?
* Do we monitor engineer kit parts usage on a daily basis, to establish parts usage and prevent wastage?
* Have we investigated the use of swap kits versus kits in which parts are replaced?
* Does our allocation of stock holding between national, local and other stock holding points minimise stock-to-stock transactions while optimising level of service on parts?
* Do we use stock cover principles for deciding stock levels?
* Do we forecast usage levels for products with rising or declining installed bases, to enable us to avoid stock shortages or obsolescence?
* Are forecasts based on data from the marketing function accurate?
* How do we allow for early signs of variation from forecast?
* Does our parts ordering procedure (from manufacturing or outside sources) minimise obsolescence while maximising level of service?
* Are repairable module movements and stocks fully integrated into our stock control system?
* Is our stock control system completely automated?
* Are the objectives of local stores carefully specified, to leave no doubt about how customer service and profitability objectives are to be met?
* Are local stock levels and the issue of parts from local stores closely controlled?

10 TARGETS AND CONTROL SYSTEMS

The effectiveness of field service must be assessed against the overall objectives that are set for it, typically achieving particular levels of customer satisfaction and/or profit (or loss avoidance!). These two kinds of target imply different strategies for field service, so there may have to be compromise before detailed operating targets are set. The nature of this compromise depends on the company's overall business objectives. For example, customer satisfaction may be vital to achieving profitable sales, in which case service may make most of its contribution to profit indirectly via customer satisfaction. In any case, short term profit maximisation at the expense of customer satisfaction is unlikely to pay in the long run.

Operating targets are set to ensure achievement of overall objectives. They normally cover factors such as response time, uptime, call rate, call length, machine breakdown frequency and engineer utilisation. Equally important are efficiency factors, especially those involving major costs, such as spare parts, operating overheads, and central repair costs. These latter are often seen by management as fixed costs. They are in fact just as variable as the other factors, though they usually take longer to change. Balancing these various targets gives many companies good profits from field service combined with a high level of customer satisfaction.

Response time
This target (varying from 2 hours or less for advanced computing equipment, to next day and longer for occasional use business equipment) is usually fixed by marketing policy. The shorter the target response time, the higher the number of engineers who need to be available to deal with faults, the lower the engineer utilisation and the higher the cost per call. Slow response may lead to customer dissatisfaction and eventual loss sales of equipment or service.

Response time must be compared with travel and repair times. Companies tend to deal with averages here, since there is no knowing what the engineer might be doing when a breakdown call is received. But we must watch the distribution of actual response times. Some engineers will be involved in long repairs, while others could be almost finishing a call. Sometimes it will be difficult to contact an engineer needed for transfer to a priority call. Where very fast response is required, a resident engineer may be necessary.

Where response time is less than average travel time plus call length, an engineer should always be available to make the call. This means that engineers are waiting, creating some spare capacity in the engineering force. If the response time is more than twice the sum of average travel time and call length, calls can be planned, to minimise travel and reduce costs. In this case there is rarely any engineer waiting time. Target response time determines the location of field engineers, the efficiency with which they can operate, and the potential for planning calls.

Waiting time can be exploited by having the engineer carry out refurbishing or repair. Some companies have reduced waiting time considerably in this way, though the different skills required of engineers and repairers may cause problems. Where design developments have made failure less catastrophic, short response times are less vital. There may therefore be a wider spread of response times in future depending on the specific failure of the equipment.

CALL DURATION

One measure of engineer effectiveness is call rate. The traditional target of one morning and one afternoon call is not enough in most sectors today. On simple repairs an average of 7 calls per day is not uncommon. This change has been caused by improved diagnosis methods, improved service documentation and test equipment, and designing equipment for repairability (e.g. exchange modules). During the call, the engineer has to carry out tasks such as:
- Finding out the customer's view of the fault.
- Placating the customer where necessary.
- Diagnosing the problem.
- Establishing which parts are necessary.
- Obtaining the parts.
- Making the repair.
- Testing the equipment.
- Recording the nature of the repair.
- Reporting back to the customer.

- Billing the customer.
- Reporting completion of task to work control.

Reducing call duration

There are many ways of reducing the time taken to complete a call. Improved pre-call diagnosis minimises delay due to returning to obtain additional parts and may reduce on-site diagnosis, repair and testing time. Module change reduces repair and testing time. Automated testing reduces testing time, increases the engineer's confidence that no other parts need attention, and should reduce the chance of calling back. However, comprehensive testing may increase the length of the individual call, while reducing call frequency.

Improved testing facilities may require modification of call length policies. Testing may be limited to critical parts (e.g. high failure, high dependence), to optimise call length and frequency. If testing systems are not used, the only test may be to run the equipment. This clearly absorbs engineer time. Study of the relationship between length of trial and detection of remaining faults will be necessary, to establish the optimum testing time. The solution also depends on the type of repair, the importance of the equipment to the customer and the pressure on the engineer. Engineers need guidelines as to how much testing to carry out. These guidelines must be consistent with call length targets, and eventually profit and customer satisfaction objectives.

Analysis of the time spent in each activity will indicate the best way to improve performance. This may lead to more training in technical skills to improve efficiency. It may also lead to training in handling customers during calls, to generate a higher level of customer satisfaction.

HANDLING THE CUSTOMER DURING THE CALL

In reporting to the customer, the engineer may try to enhance his own status rather than his company's. The customer wants an effective engineer. The engineer can achieve this status by inferring that while the equipment is poor (difficult to maintain, unreliable), he has been successful against the odds. This may encourage the customer to buy different equipment (from another supplier?). If the engineer takes the opposite approach, then the equipment seems good, but the engineer may seem less competent. The solution here may lie in a report which is objective and technical in relation to the equipment, and friendly and warm in relation to the customer.

The way the engineer provides service largely determines supplier credibility. Capable engineers who do not set out to build customer confidence may be thought to give poor service. A poor engineer can talk his way round problems and build a good rapport with the customer. In the latter case, the customer may regard the equipment as inherently unreliable when it fails again due to engineer error! So the engineer must be both personable and technically able.

The approach to the call
In making a call, the engineer's objectives should be to:
- Make an effective repair in a short time.
- Minimise the risk of a repeat call.
- Ensure that the customer is satisfied.
- Assess potential for further contracts and sales.

There are two main approaches:

The high profile
The engineer liaises with the key person in the customer organisation. This enables the decision maker to see that a good job is being done and that his company is getting value for money. By building a relationship the engineer is in a good position to avoid problems and identify sales opportunities.

The low profile
Equipment breakdown is a poor reflection on the supplier. The sooner and quicker the repair can be effected the better. Engineers should therefore have a minimum of contact with the customer on most breakdown calls. He should liaise with equipment operators if necessary.

The choice between these two depends upon the type of market and on the attitude of the customer. The high profile may be more appropriate where:
- The supplier is the only supplier of the type of equipment. The customer cannot go elsewhere. A high service cost may need to be justified.
- A comprehensive maintenance contract has been sold, and it may be necessary to check whether other equipment on the site needs attention.
- The equipment is highly reliable, so the (rare) call is taken as an opportunity for building a relationship.

- The type of equipment is known to be unreliable, whichever supplier it is obtained from, and the cost of service known to be high, but nonetheless needing justification in the eyes of senior staff.
- The equipment is critical to the customer's operation, and the customer needs to be reassured that he is being looked after by the supplier.
- A preventive maintenance programme is being carried out.

The low profile may be more appropriate where:
- Breakdown calls are frequent.
- The equipment market is highly competitive.
- The equipment is provided for casual use, and not central to the operations of the customer.
- Engineers are low grade.

Overriding all these factors are the needs of the customer. Irrespective of the 'objective' facts of the situation, some customers prefer the engineer to call on a certain senior member of staff whenever he makes a call, while others do not. Some customers like to be involved so they can see the reason for their expenditure. Others rely on feedback from their subordinates. On his customer records the local service manager may find it worth keeping a profile of the style of customers, to show which approach is more acceptable.

CALL FREQUENCY
Call frequency is determined mainly by equipment quality or complexity, but also by the quality of repair. Thus, the call frequency for a new product will be inflated, not just due to teething problems, but also because engineers are getting to know the product and how to repair it. This increases the quantity and variety of spares usage. Once the mature failure rate is established, it can be used to compare the effectiveness of different service staff or teams. Call frequency should be monitored together with repair time, since increased repair quality may be at the expense of longer call duration. However, allowance may need to be made for the use situation and type of user.

ENGINEER TIME ALLOCATION

An important criterion of the effectiveness of a service operation is how the engineer's time is used. Time use can be classified as follows:

USEFUL SERVICE TIME	Breakdown repair
	Preventive maintenance
SUPPORT ACTIVITIES	Workshop repair
	Machine installation
	Operator training
	Equipment modification
NECESSARY USED TIME	Travelling
	Training
	Administration and meetings
	Reporting
WASTED TIME	Waiting materials
	Waiting next job

Analysis of engineer time has to be treated with care. A company with a high proportion of on-site engineer time may have engineers who are slow to make repairs and spend a high proportion of their time talking to customers after repair (assuming this is not required for customer satisfaction reasons!). The interdependence between different components of time allocation may be very great, so the best general measure of effectiveness may be profit attributable to the individual or team. Analysis of individual components should therefore only be carried out under strict conditions of other factors remaining equal.

Useful service time
Breakdown Repair

The revenue earning or cost saving proportion of the engineer's day must be high. Time repairing or preventing faults has to be maximised, not the time on site. If an engineer or a team is dedicated to a particular area, eventually effectiveness will show in fewer faults and lower call-back rates. In our studies of field engineering organisations, breakdown repair time may be as high as 70% of total engineer time. Few companies achieve more than 60%, and some only 30%. But a significant proportion of companies carry out routine preventive maintenance. When this time is added to breakdown repair time, many companies achieve about 60% useful time.

Preventive Maintenance (PM)

PM takes up engineer time whether or not equipment needs repair. Our evidence shows that PM does not always reduce breakdown call frequency. But it does enable engineer workload to be planned further ahead, and gives background jobs to balance the breakdown workload. Though most companies do some PM, only in a few is the PM workload a significant part of service activities. With improved reliability of many types of equipment, PM will be confined to mechanical and electromechanical devices in the future.

If PM does reduce breakdown frequency, calls can be planned for convenience and problems resolved before they cause the inconvenience of breakdown. Some (usually electromechanical) equipment performs better given regular service. Parts which wear or degrade can be replaced before they become a problem. Engineer utilisation can be improved by reducing waiting and travel time. For other devices (often electronic) the likelihood of failure is the same throughout the equipment life. In this case there is little advantage in PM apart from customer satisfaction (see below).

Unless the cost of PM is more than offset by a reduction in breakdown service costs, the level of PM should be reduced, or justified in other ways. Spare parts usage normally increases if PM is introduced, as some parts are replaced when they have long useful lives left. PM can cause more faults than it clears. Customers are unhappy if equipment breaks down right after a PM call! Some companies do PM during breakdown calls. This avoids the travel time and may be a good compromise. Care must be taken to ensure that this does not extend the length of the engineer call too much.

Some companies use less skilled staff for PM. If skilled engineers spend the majority of repair time cleaning the equipment and making minor adjustments, using less skilled staff for these tasks saves salary costs and improves utilisation of experienced engineers. This applies particularly to equipment which is susceptible to dust and dirt (perhaps self-generated).

In summary, PM tends to be appropriate where the wear or moving parts proportion is high, where travel time or cost is large, where parts costs are low, or where the call justifies the service contract.

Customer satisfaction through PM

PM can be crucial in justifying a service contract (e.g. for very reliable equipment and for domestic appliances). If so, PM policy should depend not just on technical factors, but also on customer needs. These may include the need to see expenditure justified by a call from the service engineer. The customer may feel cheated if the engineer does not examine his equipment at least once per year. Such calls should be planned in conjunction with the department responsible for contract sales (typically before, but not too close, to the date when the renewal notice is sent out). If the call is too close, the strategy may become obvious to the customer.

Support activities

Workshop repair

In smaller companies, engineers may carry out workshop repair of subassemblies and refurbish machines. Engineer workload is smoothed where there is not a continuous flow of breakdown work. Using breakdown engineers for this work may reduce the quality of such work. If the work amounts to remanufacture, it is normally carried out better in a controlled production environment. Workshop repair by service engineers in large companies is rarer, reflecting their aims for high quality and reliability of repair.

Machine installation and operator training

Companies should have clear policies on the involvement of service engineers in installation. For some equipment, there may be an important technical task in installation (e.g. if there is a chance of the customer, sales or delivery staff making an error in installing, and if the consequences of such errors are serious). If installation requires simply positioning, connecting and starting, service engineers should not be involved. Similar considerations apply to operator training. The service engineer may need to be involved if he was involved in installation, or when asked for advice, when the customer is causing faults by misuse, or when training does not take a long time

Equipment modification

This task, normally allotted to service, occurs when faults are found with existing equipment, when the customer receives modification as part of his agreement with the company (e.g. automatic up-dating), or where the customer has paid for a specific modification. Unless the equipment is dangerous or causing severe problems to the customer (either through malfunction or delayed enhancement of functions), these modifications are not normally high priority, particularly if they do not yield additional profit. They should preferably be carried out during a maintenance visit to avoid unnecessary costs. Where a special call is necessary, it should be planned in the same way as PM.

Necessary used time

This covers activities which are necessary for the operation of the service department, but which do not generate revenue.

Travelling

For most companies, this is a major absorber of time, and a major opportunity to reduce costs. In some companies, travel time is over 50% of the engineers' time. The factors which increase travelling time are:
- Short response time .
- Poor call planning.
- Limited engineer skill.
- Spare parts availability.
- Return to base policy.
- Dispersion of installed base.

With the exception of the last of these factors, most of them are at least partially controlled by the service operation, through its policies on organisation structure, staffing, planning, control, communications and spares inventory. In some companies, the failure to deal with all these aspects in an integrated way has driven up travel time. Revisiting all these aspects, with the objective of reducing travel time (and eventually improving profit) can yield major improvements in engineer utilisation. For example, abolishing return to base policies (or even morning report to base policies) combined with improved communication systems may yield major improvements.

Training

Engineers need training in various skills, from basic product technologies, through equipment up-dates, to time management and customer relations skills. Investment in training is valuable in achieving better performance during calls. Improvements in educational technology are enabling training to take place more cost-effectively. Video disc-based systems permit more inter-active training in service branches, enabling the use of central training schools to be reduced. Package-based training in time management and customer relations is providing management with low cost, time-effective solutions in these areas. The need for training should be audited via statistics on return calls and call duration (for technical training), variability between engineers in effective time allocation (for time management) and customer satisfaction ratings (for customer relations skills). Service management training is important too. Managers should be trained in all the above, plus man-management skills. Once again, improved educational technology is opening up avenues to low cost, time-effective training for first line managers.

Administration and meetings

As with training, time spent on meetings is a matter of judgement. Employee involvement in departmental activities may be very important for engineers from outlying areas or in organisations where the workload is very high. Regular meetings between engineer and manager are important to convey policies to engineers and for feedback on the situation in the field. Reporting should be as automated as possible, with meetings concentrating on exceptions. If meetings turn into acrimonious affairs, they are not fulfilling their function. Good managers can direct individuals toward their targets without regular discord. However meetings do waste time, especially if a large number are attending. So meetings should be small, have a well defined purpose, and only last long enough to cover the discussion points in an adequate manner.

Reporting

Reporting should be carried out with a minimum of effort by both creator and recipient of information. Systems should be designed so engineers have little to write other than nature of fault, of repair and parts used. The service engineer is not always expert at filling in paperwork! We do not want them to waste time on this when they can be earning revenue for the company.

Wasted time
Waiting for parts

Engineers can rarely carry all the spares for a day's calls. Work control procedures may enable another call to be made while parts are delivered to the original site. If the engineer returns to collect a spare which is unavailable at base, he may have waiting time. In smaller companies, this may be used to repair or refurbish equipment, or disassemble old equipment for use as spares.

Waiting next job

As with time spent waiting for materials, the true size of waiting time can be masked if engineers carry out work at the local branch. Care must be taken to ensure that the amount of work completed justifies the time spent. High engineer waiting time can be caused by:

- Short response time.
- Low machine population.
- Imbalance of engineer skills.
- Small branch size.
- Improved machine reliability.
- Poor call co-ordination.

Waiting time is a key area for investigation for ways of improving efficiency, even though the amount reported may be very small. We need to balance the cost of engineer travelling, wasted time, response time and the ability to use slack time of engineers for other work.

MANAGEMENT REPORTING

Effective control requires good reporting systems, to collect information for controlling operations and for longer term planning. The high availability of detailed operational information to line management may make it difficult to direct priorities toward medium term targets (e.g. customer satisfaction) over short term objectives (e.g. response time). Data is also required for fault analysis and machine history, as follows:

- Machine number and equipment type.
- Symptoms of breakdown and cause of fault.
- Parts used in diagnosis.
- Parts used in repair.
- Adjustments made.
- State of the equipment.
- Other repairs made or required.
- Time of arrival on site and departure.

This information comes from the visit reporting system and is converted into call and cost information. Short term control is maintained by monitoring the day's workload through records such as:

- Daily jobs outstanding.
- Calls requiring escalation.
- Unavailable parts.

Longer term control should be via the targets listed at the beginning of this chapter. They can also be used to check comparative performance (e.g. between regions). Too much information can swamp managers and is not effective. Too general results can lead to inequitable comparisons.

Unless real time systems are used, financial reports appear after the period in question. This delay is one reason for using operational targets as opposed to financial ones. Problems may have changed before the information is available, so reports may be used negatively to shift the blame for shortcomings to other departments. For cost control to be a meaningful part of service control, results have to be available as the events happen, and in sufficient detail.

TARGETS

Targets of all kinds should provide a challenge to managers and staff, but not be unrealistic. It also helps if they are agreed with the individuals for whom they are set. If an individual is given a target, he should be able to control the main determinants of the situation affected by the target. It is no use giving a branch manager the task of reducing his local stock if it is being replenished automatically from the national warehouse.

Many companies use information to rectify current problems, but not to plan to improve overall effectiveness. Tactics to rectify current problems may improve effectiveness, but systematic solutions are rarely achieved in this way. Targets should provide incentives to improve effectiveness via better systems and controls. Just as targets are changed to suit the market, so systems should be continually modified to provide the best controls in the circumstances. For each control target, there should be a rolling monitor of results so that long term trends can be reviewed. There is little use in collecting and collating management information unless it is used for feedback to the field, or for technical or management action. Management information should be brief, showing totals and highlighting the few key positive and negative deviations.

Management targets should be primarily financial, backed by operating targets (e.g. calls per engineer month, call length, response times and manpower ratios) to enable financial goals to be reached.

Role of comparative analyses

Comparison between areas may highlight major anomalies. Comparison between different companies in the same industry helps by introducing a wider range of approaches to similar situations, though comparisons should allow for differences in customers, equipment and operating environments.

CHECKLIST FOR CHAPTER 10

Targets

* Do we give our engineers a balanced set of targets, preventing undue emphasis on any one target (and associated distortions of emphasis) and attempts by engineers to exaggerate achievement of targets?
* Are their targets clearly linked to key service objectives (e.g. profit, customer satisfaction)? Is the link clear to engineers and customers?
* Is the choice between high and low engineer profile during the call taken on the right grounds (i.e. customer preferences)?
* Is analysis of performance against targets used for long term planning to increase effectiveness, as well as for short term tactical actions?

Engineer time allocation

* Have we examined the benefits and costs of preventive maintenance and in-branch repair?
* Are work control procedures flexible enough to allow local changes to optimise engineer time allocation (e.g. partial preventive maintenance)?
* Are modifications scheduled for preventive maintenance or other calls?
* Do we ensure that engineers are only involved in machine installation and operator training when absolutely necessary?
* Do we understand all the determinants of travel time (response times, call planning, engineer skills match to needs, parts availability, return to base policies, installed base dispersion)? Would small changes in several determinants lead to substantial savings in travel time?
* Are we using the latest, most cost effective training techniques (e.g. computerised training, self-paced packages)?
* Is time spent in meetings and preparing reports well justified?
* Is engineer wait for parts minimised by efficient inventory management?
* If we reduced the number of inventory echelons, would engineers be able to carry more parts, reducing time waiting for or collecting parts?
* Do we understand all the determinants of engineer waiting time (short response times, low machine populations, imbalance of engineer skills, small branch size, and poor call co-ordination)? Would small changes in more than one element yield significant savings?

11 FINANCIAL PLANNING AND CONTROL

Service uses resources (e.g. people, equipment, supplies) to provide an output, customer service. Service often forms a major element of company cost, revenues and profit. In a competitive business, activities should be managed primarily by their contribution to company survival, cash flow and profit. In some companies, the formal objective of service is to deliver a given level of service subject to a cost constraint. In others, service has full profit responsibility. In most companies, awareness of service's contribution to cash flow is growing, with significant advantages arising from payment in advance through service contracts, and significant penalties arising from cash tied up in inflated parts inventories. Service management must understand financial and accounting techniques for controlling costs, optimising cash flow or increasing profitability. This chapter summarises the elements of financial planning and control most relevant to service management.

COST CLASSIFICATION

Cost analysis provides indicators of how resources are being used, and where reallocation of resources can help meet targets. Most companies use one or two methods of cost classification for reporting purposes. For management purposes, there are many methods. Cost classification may relate to:

- Historical period to which they relate (e.g. replacement costs can be reckoned by what it would cost to replace something today, or what it cost to buy in the first place).
- Type of resource (e.g. labour, parts, materials, transport).
- Activity for which they are incurred (e.g. field service, parts holding).
- Location of resource use (e.g. branch, area).
- Type of equipment supported by the resource.
- Whether allocatable to individual units of output (direct or indirect).
- Whether they vary with output (fixed or variable).
- Whether avoidable or not (e.g. within a given period, or by discontinuing a certain activity - contractual questions may be important here).
- Whether controllable by particular staff (this can be hard to define - many costs which an individual cannot control are influenced by him, either via advice to more senior staff, or by influence on peers).

- Whether engineered or managed (engineered costs may be known as 'product inherent', and in service usually relate to parts).
- Whether average or marginal (average costs being total costs of an activity divided by the number of units produced by the activity, marginal being the cost of producing an extra unit).
- Whether monetary costs (representing an actual outlay) or opportunity costs (representing opportunities) are foregone by using them - this might apply to equipment which is fully depreciated but is still saleable).

Some classifications are not absolute. Thus, costs may be semi-variable, being fixed for output within a certain range, and rising for higher outputs.

Fixed and variable costs

Most accounting systems are based on the distinction between fixed and variable costs. The distinction between the two is relative. Total engineer time is fixed for decisions with a horizon less than the termination period of engineer contracts. Beyond that period, total engineer time is variable. For a given job, where time spent is time not dedicated to other jobs, engineer time is a variable cost. Service premises are fixed for the lease period, but variable if they can be used for sales activities (if there is a demand for additional sales space).

Complexity of cost structure

As in most service industries, the cost structure of most service operations is very complex, lacking the simplicity of factory throughput as a fixed measure of output. Much of what a service branch does is not a consequence of its own actions, while the true costs of any particular activity are difficult to establish. While we may know the average cost of delivering service to customers, individual costs are difficult to establish in practice. Even if we can cost a particular call, it is difficult to forecast the costs of servicing a given customer with given equipment - so much depends on when he calls, what the nature of the call is, how long the problem takes to resolve, what parts will be used, and so on. However, we must cut through these complexities if we are to establish the financial viability of the service organisation. Break-even analysis is one technique used to do this.

BREAK-EVEN ANALYSIS

A high proportion of the costs of most service organisations is fixed in the short term, making them very sensitive to volume. If revenue falls relative to expectations, pressure immediately falls upon variable costs. The main variable costs in service are engineer remuneration, travelling, and parts (see Table 11.1). All these are variable and at least partly under field service control (the marketing function is likely to have a major influence on the level of service delivered). The problem may be caused by unsuccessful marketing of service (price too high or low, not enough contracts sold), so the marketing function may bear some responsibility for the problem.

Table 11.1 Variable costs

Engineer remuneration	Travelling costs	Parts
Salary	Petrol	Value of parts fitted
Overtime	Repairs	Value of consumables used
Allowances	Tax and insurance	Excess cost of emergency deliveries
National Insurance	Depreciation	
Tax	Hire charges	
Pension contribution	Fares	
Personal insurance	Private car allowance	
Expenses		

Fixed costs should also be scrutinised (see Table 11.2). These can be split into direct costs to branches, service centres or other bases from which engineers operate, and central operating costs. Most of these costs are local and under the control of branch service management. Local fixed costs include premises, supervision, stores, call receipt/work control (unless these are central) and transport.

Table 11.2 Fixed costs

Direct fixed costs	Company fixed costs
Supervision and support	**Company overhead**
National insurance	**Direct operating**
Tax	Transport
Travelling expenses	Computer time
Service marketing	**Apportioned costs**
Advertising	Management and administration
Promotion	R&D
Accomodation	Data processing
Rent, rates and insurance	Personnel
Security	Financial costs (Audit, bad debt, debt collection, corporate taxes, interest)
Repairs	Accounts
Heating and Lighting	Advertising and marketing
Telephone	General supplies
Stationery	Buildings
Consumables	Purchasing
Repair centre	
Salary and wage costs	
Rent, rates and insurance	
Purchases	
Technical back up	
Depreciation	
Property and equipment	
Vehicles	
Stockholding costs	
Stock obsolescence provision	
Stock finance	

Central costs may cause local managers some concern. If figures are published within the company, the local manager may see his good margin much reduced by high company overheads. These may be charges for work done, or allocation of direct charges, supporting activities such as logistic support and transport, purchasing, systems, cost accounting, central technical support, and central management. The local manager is rarely in a position to see the full benefit of these services. If service branches are operated as profit centres, there may be difficulties in allocating central costs. Often, this is done on the basis of the area occupied, turnover, or headcount. It should as near as possible reflect the real use of resources. For example, if the branch has a high concentration of high revenue but difficult to service equipment, then the frequent use of central technical support should be charged.

BUDGETS

The budget provides a mechanism for controlling service. It is built on estimated revenue and cost flows. There may also be a cash flow budget. Most service operations have good national budgeting systems. The way the budget is broken into local budgets varies. Some companies are not keen to give such information to local managers. Without such disclosure, it is hard for managers to operate on any but the most simple physical controls. Inventory costs are usually disclosed. They may be more crucial, particularly if more than one stock level is under branch control (e.g. engineer and local stock).

Cash flow

Many companies pass through a cycle in their treatment of service. They start by providing service as support to sales. They then realise the profit and long term sales advantages of applying professional management to service, and introduce profit and customer satisfaction targets. Finally, service emerges as a key contributor to all business objectives, including cash flow, which has received much attention as an indicator of business effectiveness as the real cost of cash has risen. As companies become more aware of the cost of funds, the pressure on service operations to generate and collect cash increases, leading to cash budgeting. Where this is absent, control is exercised by the finance function regulating or influencing those service decisions which affect cash flow.

Asset-based measurements

Service is a major absorber of assets, through spare parts inventories, test equipment, repairable modules and real estate. If equipment is often rented, service affects return on assets (RoA) through customer satisfaction. Dissatisfied customers may cancel rental contracts, reducing the return on assets, either because the equipment cannot be rented again (in which case profit has to be allocated to writing down the equipment), or because of the increased cost of refurbishing it and/or renting out to another customer.

Depreciation

An important element of asset-based measurements is depreciation. If the real effect of depreciation can be reduced (e.g. by avoiding inflated parts stocks which depreciate rapidly due to obsolescence), RoA will increase.

Using financial data

Some service managers treat financial data with suspicion and distrust. Yet financial data provide a real opportunity for service management to improve their effectiveness. A good financial reporting system, together with the appropriate computing facilities (e.g. microcomputers running data base, financial modelling and spread sheet packages), allows the service manager to improve service effectiveness by helping to:

- Model change, by evaluating effects of changes in the environment, or the effects of different service policies on profits, costs and cash.
- Provide management ratios for local managers to work to.
- Identify major cost elements, and the sensitivity of service profit to variations in them.
- Ensure availability of the right cost data for contract pricing decisions, whether for general contracts or individual customers.
- Identify true costs and profitability of providing service for different customers, equipment, to different areas or market segments, or under different types of service contract.
- Establish productivity of different resources in terms of profit and cash produced, overall and for different products, areas, etc.
- Identify where cheaper or more effective resources can be substituted.
- Enhance staff motivation by demonstrating their profit contribution.

- Improve cost control, by providing more rapid feed back of information on service costs.
- Establish the true contribution of service to overall business success.

FINANCIAL INFORMATION SYSTEMS

If the service function has enough freedom of action, it will make decisions which affect overall company performance. Thus, the decision whether to market a certain type of service contract affects cash flow. A new contract may involve a higher price, but weaker cash flow (e.g. payment on service rather than in advance). The service information system needs to measure the cash flow situation if the new form of contract is to be properly evaluated. Similarly, different levels of service will require different asset profiles (e.g. spare parts inventories). What is the RoA implication of a higher level of service delivered under a premium contract (i.e. higher price and higher assets)? How are parts costs written down (by some simple accounting rule, or one that reflects their true obsolescence rate)? Failure to pay attention to service's return on assets may lead to a lower company RoA.

Asset-related information

The situation is complicated by the existence of repairable modules and refurbishable machines. Irrespective of written down values, equipment which is saleable/rentable does have an opportunity cost, and companies which treat these assets in terms of their opportunity cost (the price that could be obtained for them implicitly, via reincorporation through service, or explicitly, through sale) may demonstrate a much higher RoA.

Whatever the profitability in using assets, asset turn is a key measure. Service is often one of the most asset-intense functions, not only in spare parts but also sometimes with responsibility for equipment inventories (new or refurbished). But what asset turn is attributable to service? The normal measure would be asset-related service revenue divided by the average value of assets. However, given the high labour content of many service operations, this measure would make the most labour intense service products look very favourable (assuming that this labour intensity resulted in a correspondingly high price for service!)

If labour content does not influence the calculation too much, it makes sense to consider fast versus slow moving parts in terms of return on assets and asset turn, and price accordingly. So while the engineer's solution to slow moving parts might be to have a different stocking procedure, the alternative solution is to make sure that the margin makes up for the slow stock turn, by pricing them higher. However, this assumes power over price, normal in the case of time and materials service, but not for full contracts.

The information system should include data covering the above points. If the appropriate mark-up is not imputed to slower moving parts, asset management procedures may break down, since the economic cost of the part may never be known, and the incentive to change the situation removed. For example, lack of profitability of contracts involving many slow moving parts which have to be kept in stock may be ignored, and the contracts stillvactively marketed. The ideal situation in a parts operation is to have all parts equally reliable, since the same margins, stock and delivery procedures can then be applied to each. If reliability varies greatly, the customer's sense of value for money may be offended if parts are priced according to the cost of holding them.

Much of this logic applies to sourcing of parts from third parties, affecting choice of parts (negotiating supplier prices) and who shall hold the stock (the parts supplier may be persuaded to supply on a just-in-time basis).

Cost allocation

Debates usually arise over how the information system treats cost allocation. What are the true costs of servicing one type of machine rather than another, if they are both serviced by the same engineer? Should the engineer's cost be allocated between the two machines according to the time spent servicing them? Not if one is more complex than another, necessitating more training for the engineer! Not if one never requires servicing urgently, while the other always demands rapid response! Because of the difficulty of allocating costs, some argue that contribution margin is the best measure. In this approach, only the most direct costs (e.g. parts, labour) are allocated, and other costs (e.g. travel time) not allocated. This prevents termination of activities which, though not yielding a net margin, are making a contribution to the overall overheads of the service operation (or at least, if they are deleted, they need to be replaced by other products).

Variance analysis

Variance analysis is often used as a technique to identify machines, areas, and so on whose costs are abnormally high or low. This process must be used in combination with insight. It is not sufficient merely to apply pressure on those areas where costs are high, without first investigating the reason for the variance. Management by exception should be applied here.

USING FINANCIAL INFORMATION

Financial data is useful, but may not yield its full benefit if it is not part of a total management control system. In turn, a management control system may misfire if it does not form part of a total business system for achieving objectives. This requires:

- A clear set of business goals.
- A break-down of business goals into functional areas and then into individual responsibilities within the service function.
- A clear plan of action to attain goals.
- Identification of resource and revenue implications of each plan. This is normally done via budgets, the principal weapon of co-ordination and control - the budget should serve as declaration of objectives and ties in service efforts with those of finance and other functions.
- Allocating cost responsibility via budgets, by area, product, customer, and so forth. The degree of delegation, selectiveness of review and extent of management by exception can transform a mechanistic process into a creative process.
- Adopting standards for achieving plan (in fast changing environments, care should be taken to avoid rigidity, since productivity standards may depend upon factors such as increasing automation of service tasks).
- An information system which measures actual performance and compares actual with predetermined standards, using (amongst other techniques) analysis of variances and trends, then passes on results to relevant level of management. A vital component of this system is the report, so we need to establish how many we need, why, how frequently and whether they should be complete or by exception.
- Taking corrective or adaptive action.

A service controller?

In larger service organisations, it may be highly beneficial to have a specialist service controller, responsible for all the financial aspects of the service operation. Financially qualified, but with intimate knowledge of the service operation, such an individual can provide a vital policy and communication bridge between service and finance functions, as well as helping the service function to improve its profitability.

CHECKLIST FOR CHAPTER 11

* Is there absolute clarity on the planned contribution of service to overall financial objectives, absolutely and relative to other functions?
* Is the contribution of service to cash flow and asset usage understood and targeted?
* Have we considered appointing a service controller with total responsibility for the financial performance of the service operation?
* Are the financial objectives of the service operation in balance with customer service objectives?

Cost classification

* Do the cost classifications we use in service management and planning relate as closely as possible to the real cost of service resources?
* Do our classifications allow us to analyse service costs by all the dimensions we need (e.g. area, equipment product, service product, market segment, individual customer, type of service resource used)?
* Do our classifications allow us to analyse unit cost variations for different service activity levels?
* Do we understand how the service profit margin may change with changing activity levels?
* Does the allocation of central costs correspond as nearly as possible with the use of central resources by different service activities?

Budgets

* Do service budgets include cash flow and asset usage elements as well as cost and revenue elements?
* Have we considered the advantages and disadvantages of allocating profit (i.e. cost and revenue) budgets to all units of the service operation?
* Do our budgets provide incentives to all members of staff to improve efficiency without damaging customer service?
* Are our business goals broken down into the functional and other units to which budgets are allocated, such that there is a clear relation between budget achievement and business goal achievement?
* Are our budgeting procedures reviewed occasionally to check for their suitability in a changing business and technical environment?

Using financial data

Do we use financial data to :

* Establish the true contribution of service to profit, cash flow and return on assets?
* Identify the sensitivity of service costs and revenue to major changes in the service business?
* Identify under-utilised assets?
* Model the overall effects of changes in the service business?
* Provide management ratios for all levels of service management?
* Improve cost control, by providing as rapid as possible feedback of performance against budget?
* Identify where cheaper or more effective resources can be used?
* Enhance staff motivation by demonstration contribution to profit?
* Ensure availability of the right financial data for service pricing decisions, particularly for new service and equipment products, for serving new market segments, or for individual customer pricing?
* Check profit and cash productivity of individual service resources?

12 PRODUCTIVITY, PERFORMANCE AND PLANNING

Most service management tasks relate to two types of objective:
- Performance e.g. revenue, level of service.
- Productivity - performance relative to the cost of achieving it.

These two objectives often conflict, with the finance function often playing a key role in deciding between the two. For example, if more engineers are needed to improve the level of service, the finance function may object on cash flow or budgetary grounds.

The need to increase productivity

In any industry where the price level is falling or forecast to fall, service costs are likely to come under pressure (whether through technical progress or competitive entry by other suppliers, third party maintenance companies, or distributors). If service costs are rising as a proportion of total (not just service) installed-base originating revenue, there is a clear need to work on service productivity. If profits are very high and the market expanding rapidly, with robust price levels, service productivity may not be an issue today. However, it may be tomorrow. In such cases, it should at least be documented in the service plan, together with early warning signals relating to the need to improve service productivity.

Table 12.1 Service inputs and outputs

Measures of output	Measures of input
Customer satisfaction	Net assets (fixed and current)
Net service revenue	Current costs (absolute)
Customer loyalty	Number of engineers
Level of service	Number of service branches
Etc.	Etc.

Input and output measures

There are many measures of productivity, which is defined broadly as the relation between inputs and outputs, such as those listed in Table 12.1. Revenue is a commonly used measure of output, but in some cases, the service function is effectively picking up profit generated by sales activities, so using revenue as a measure can generate a false sense of performance. To put this another way, price may not be a good measure of output, since the customer is captive and therefore has no option but to pay!

Service productivity - adding value?

Service exists to add value to the customer, or at least prevent value added deteriorating, so the output measure should relate to this value added. In a world with no cross-subsidy between product sale and service, and where every customer makes a conscious choice on service, this value added would be at a minimum equal to the price paid for service. Nobody would buy service if it was worth less than the price charged for it, and many would pay more than they are actually asked to pay.

'What would you be prepared to pay?' questions are unreliable as ways of establishing value. The option of experimenting with price to establish the value of service is difficult to use in practice. So it may be better to use a measure based upon customer satisfaction questionnaires (e.g. as an answer to the question "Is the level of service you receive better than the minimum you would expect for this price?"). However, even this question is too complex, so the best practical measure might be in terms of the proportion of customers who state that they are more than satisfied with the level of service received. This measure will also avoid bias if the price paid for service is not closely related to the benefit (for example, if service price is part of a package deal which includes low equipment cost). However, to many service managers, this kind of measure seems far too vague. Given their engineering origin, preferred measures may be in terms of size of installed base per engineer, or equipment uptime, despite the fact that customers may not be aware of what uptime levels have been reached.

Service inputs

Measuring service inputs is easier. The appropriate measure is normally in terms of overall current input costs (labour, parts, etc.), but partial productivity ratios (labour productivity, parts productivity) can be very instructive in isolating areas where inputs are too high or low relative to output, or where the input mix is incorrect (e.g. if an engineer is replacing too many parts on each call). For this kind of analysis, it is useful to measure marginal as well as average productivities, since these indicate the costs or benefits of small changes. We also need to use asset-based measures.

Types of productivity measure

We can classify the resulting productivity measures in the following way:

Level of service measures: e.g. number of satisfied customers per branch or per engineer.

Financial measures: e.g. return on assets, asset turn, profit margin on service revenue, revenue per unit service spend. These tie in closely to company financial objectives.

Semi-financial measures: - e.g. revenue per serviceman or equipment serviced per unit service spend. These indicate the relationship between financial objectives and items more easily understood and controlled by service, such as manpower, units serviced, etc.

Physical productivity measures: e.g. units serviced or number of calls per time period.

Seen in this way, there are many ways of increasing service productivity. These include not only aggregate changes in costs and prices, but also change in the mix of service policies. Thus, it may make sense to subcontract certain elements of service because these offer a much better relationship between net service revenue and costs, without altering customer satisfaction.

Non-input-output measures

Most productivity measures are input-output (e.g. revenue per serviceman). Other categories of measure are input-input (e.g. managers per engineer, or parts stock/engineer) or output-output (proportion of machines under service contract). In a mature business operating with stable markets and products, management has had the time to evolve a clear set of productivity measures.

Elsewhere, this is rarely so, and productivity measures should be monitored for suitability for summarising service effectiveness.

PRODUCTIVITY CONTROL
Ratio proliferation versus delegation
The search for productivity can lead to a proliferation of ratios. It may be better to avoid too many central measures of productivity and attempt to control them, instead delegating responsibility for productivity to local level, subject to control by overall financial productivity measures (e.g. service profitability). The main risk here is of choosing the wrong financial measure. Controlling by service cost as a proportion of revenue, or by profit margin (net or contribution) can result in a lower level of service than required to sustain the customer base, or in ignoring the asset input of different policies - a service policy which apparently delivers a high margin may be very wasteful of assets (e.g. parts inventory). To avoid the former, it may be necessary to combine a performance measure (e.g. customer satisfaction rating) with a productivity measure (e.g. service profit). To avoid the latter, asset measures need to be combined with margin measures.

Devoting substantial resources to finding the best measure for productivity and then to measuring it may not be wise. Productivity can improve without being precisely measured at every level. In the end, the objective is increased profit for the whole organisation. If all those involved in the search for service productivity understand that profitability is helped by increasing outputs relative to inputs, whatever inputs and outputs they happen to work with, this may by itself do the job, particularly if it is applied as a general test of the acceptability of components of the service plan.

Short and long term objectives
Some outputs, such as customer loyalty, tend to relate to longer term business objectives. It is easy to sacrifice them to make short term cost savings, particularly if the relationship between immediate and longer term objectives is not clearly stated. In a good service plan, there should be little room for doubt about the trade-off between different objectives.

Productivity analysis
One approach to improving productivity is to examine the marginal productivity of different elements of the service mix, to see whether resources can be

switched to improve overall output. For example, it may be appropriate to switch an engineer between areas with different levels of performance per engineer. Much depends on the rate at which returns to an additional engineer diminish in the two areas. The workload in the first area might be quite even, allowing fine tuning of engineer allocation, and consequent high productivity. In the second area, the workload may be very uneven, such that an extra engineer does not make much impact on performance. Other solutions may lie in reallocating responsibilities by changing area boundaries or equipment specialisation. Tables based on performance distribution are essential tools in productivity analysis, but need to be interpreted and used carefully. The way in which a group of engineers works together, or generates its motivation, may have a much greater impact than fine tuning.

Productivity improvement

There is no optimum way of improving service productivity. Different company styles produce different solutions. Centralised companies have centralised solutions, decentralised companies decentralised solutions. One common factor which underlies success in achieving improved service productivity is applying recent advances in computing, communications and office automation to improve administrative effectiveness, call handling, parts inventory management, planning processes, thereby saving time and resources and improving competitiveness and service. This does not mean vast data bases - successful automation may enable companies to do with less regular reporting, freeing time that was devoted to producing reports.

Productivity initiatives

Productivity initiatives (e.g. cost reduction schemes) may become more widespread as the need to save costs and improve performance increases. Whether top-down or bottom-up (with employee-involvement), objectives should be clear and designed to be acceptable to those affected by the scheme. If a scheme is seen as putting more into profits by reducing headcount, its acceptance is likely to be low, and it may not produce results. Since the objective is nearly always to improve service competitiveness, it is sensible to embed cost-saving objectives firmly in the context of improving productivity by getting increased performance at constant costs, rather than constant performance at reduced cost. If the objective is seen as making the company more competitive, and hence opening opportunities for increased performance, then the chance of success is higher.

Management productivity

Management inefficiency causes inefficiencies elsewhere in the organisation, either directly or through the demonstration effect. Slack practices, unclear objectives or standards of performance, or wasted funds reduce the impact of a productivity drive. In larger companies, there is a 'middle management barrier' to productivity. Whether productivity is being driven hard from the top or not, the ranks of middle management need to be involved all along. Their actions may determine whether productivity improves. Supervisors (e.g. service team leaders, area service managers, parts store managers) must be prepared for their role. This implies communicating to them the objectives of increasing productivity and how they are to be achieved, and may imply formal training. Productivity responsibility normally implies some cost responsibility. Some supervisors may be used only to performance responsibility (e.g. response time, customer satisfaction).

Service productivity is hard to improve quickly, especially in larger companies. Service productivity is not just a technical factor, but a result of how people work, which has to be changed to improve productivity.

THE PLANNING PROCESS AND EFFECTIVENESS

Performance objectives are usually specified in the service plan. The breadth and level of detail of specification depends on whether the company has a top-down or bottom-up planning process.

Top-down service planning

Top-down planning is often a tight and disciplined process, typical of larger suppliers. The plan covers a large number of service variables, and is put together by a central team, which requires major inputs of forecasts, market and machine data. There is little attempt to reach a concensus with those whose activities are being planned and controlled. This approach has certain advantages, if well used. It enables control and direction actions to be carried out relatively smoothly and with some certainty. Objectives and targets can be well communicated within an accepted framework. A good basis exists for understanding the effect on the business of changes in the business environment or in service policy. If the level of management skill in the departments whose activities are being planned is not high then assuming the service planners to be skilled enough, it provides a way of getting the company to behave as if all were skilled.

The weakness in this approach is its dependence on the supply and quality of data. If data is unavailable or inaccurate, quantification is still produced, but it may be unsound. Unsound policy-making or unreliable data can throw the whole plan off balance. Another weakness of this approach is the process itself. Because it has a rigid timetable, problems not addressed are left unaddressed. The focus may be on the process of planning, rather than on the service challenge which the plan is supposed to help the company meet.

This approach can lead to over-centralised service management, on the grounds that planners are the only ones with all the facts, and therefore they should decide. Of course, few managers' ability to make good decisions rests upon having a large compendium of possibly out of date facts! Furthermore, central planning staff may miss key messages about why some policies are easy or cheaper to implement, and others not. Ignorance of implementation and productivity problems is common with central planning functions.

Bottom-up planning

This is a looser system, where more responsibility is delegated to field service units. These units then function within an agreed budget and general objectives, and commit to certain levels of service performance and profitability, but are not required to give complete account of all their activities to the service planning or central unit. In such a system, the control of service is not via the plan, but via motivation and reward, which relate to a few key control parameters (e.g. profit, revenue, customer satisfaction). The focus of all units is kept on service objectives, not on fulfilling a particular plan handed down from the centre. It is cheaper and tends to produce a faster response to problems.

A disadvantage of this system is the high level of skill and motivation required in managers of units to which responsibility is delegated. If these are not present, service performance suffers. At worst, there may be a general loss of control. The staffing and reward system for such a planning philosophy clearly has to be very different. Also, because it works within a simple set of objectives and constraints, if these are misspecified, there are no other controls which come into play.

A variant of this approach is one in which service units make their own plans, according to the general objectives and constraints laid down for them, and communicate them upwards for validation. They are then held to these plans, and the main role for central service planning is to assemble and validate plans. This mode of planning has a major advantage in gaining commitment of implementers, since they are implementing their own plans. However, it has some of the disadvantages of tops-down planning (e.g. less flexibility) and of bottom-up planning (e.g. dependence on skills).

Each approach can work in different situations. Whether they work depends on internal factors (whether the service organisation has the right structure, controls and incentives to work the particular approach, whether the information system is adequate to support the approach) and external factors (e.g. speed/predictability of change in markets and technology). In an unstable market, where central plans risk rapid outdating, the bottoms-up or loose approach may be more appropriate, whereas in a stable situation, the tight approach may yield better profits.

PLANNING, TARGETING AND PRODUCTIVITY

Engineer targeting depends on predicting user requirements/perceptions on levels of service, and the technical requirements of equipment (e.g. failure rates, repair times), for the business as a whole and for individual service areas. The targeting procedure should reflect the forecastability of the market. If the determinants of customer satisfaction are not known or understood, then it makes little sense to target a service force on increasing customer satisfaction by a particular amount.

Working to achieve detailed 'top-down' targets can be expensive in terms of productivity. It can result in a higher level of service being delivered than is required, and may produce other problems (e.g. neglected preventive maintenance and increased service costs). There is also a danger of getting customers used to a level of service which cannot be sustained profitably. Where user requirements have not settled down, targeting should perhaps be less acutely detailed than in a more stable market. However, parts and resource constraints rarely allow targets to be completely flexible. The responsibility for achieving different service objectives may be split between different levels of the organisation. Uptime or response time targets may be given to engineers, while parts cost and other resource responsibilities may be given to management, to devise less expensive repair standards and incentives for engineers to adhere to them.

Separating budgeting from targeting

Some companies fail to separate budgeting from targeting. If products have long mean times between failure, if the installed base is sufficiently varied for there to be unexpected peaks and troughs in the demand for service, and if the phasing of targets is based on a monthly or even three-monthly budget, it is difficult for the engineer and service manager to make the right trade-offs between meeting this month's targets on resource usage and providing a good service to the customer. In such cases, less frequent control and review of field service may be right, unless the impact of variable demand for service is allowed for in the targeting process. But there has to be enough pressure in the targeting system to ensure efficiency. The balance between cost and performance objectives cannot be dealt with solely via the service force targeting mechanism. It has to be dealt with via field management, whose own targets and compensation should encourage them to restore balance between performance and productivity.

MANAGEMENT AND CONTROL

To exercise effective control the service manager should understand:

1. How the workload is likely to evolve.
2. How well his engineers deal with the workload.
3. Whether they use the right customer care approach for different users.
4. What obstructs productivity/performance (e.g. inadequate administrative support, documentation, overloading servicemen with administration, weak or unbalanced incentives)
5. Whether particular engineers are weak, and whether they need help by management intervention, field accompaniment, training or firing.

How a service manager approaches his task is conditioned by his own background, experience and attitudes, and the amount of independence he has, the number of variables on which he is controlled, the nature and frequency of control, and the reward and incentive structure within which he operates. Much hangs upon how his own management relates to him. A service manager who is highly aware of the need to divide attention between servicing old equipment and maintaining high standards on newly installed, sensitive equipment is unlikely to get the balance right if he is under weekly pressure to maintain exactly the same standards on all equipment.

Purpose and method of control

One aim of control is to detect underperforming areas, products, or engineers (to take corrective action) and overperforming areas, products, or engineers (to identify additional opportunities). One method is via a phased plan for key variables. Performance is then measured against plan. Measures used include service revenue and costs, parts usage, parts inventory, customer satisfaction indices, response times, uptime, repair times, manpower, etc. This plan may be phased frequently (e.g. monthly) or infrequently (e.g. yearly). In a top-down planned company, the number of measures is likely to be much higher than under other planning approaches.

Control measures

Measures should be chosen in the light of two key purposes of measurement, namely, a way of understanding the business, and for incentive, control and motivation. Using the service plan as the basis for phasing and to judge performance places much onus on the plan to be realistic. If it is not, performance measures against plan are relatively meaningless. If the installed base and customer needs are changing rapidly, and it is recognised that the plan is only an approximate guide to activity, it is more appropriate to use straight performance comparisons. These include comparisons of the same measure over time, and comparisons between parts of the service organisation.

Choice of control measures

The best control measures bear a close relation to customers' measures of service. If users are unaware of response times, but sensitive to uptime, it is important not to control engineers on response time, even though it affects uptime, since this may dissuade them from improving diagnosis prior to calling (and probably from reducing broken calls by picking up parts).

Performance measurement (whether or not against plan) should distinguish between policy failure (e.g. the service force being asked to do something infeasible or contrary to user needs) and individual underachievement, and between policy undercall and individual overachievement. The difficulty here is that a general policy problem may only emerge through the performance of some units. Undertargeting may show via extreme overperformance of some units rather than slight over-target performance of all units (e.g. if the unreliability of equipment used in a particular way has been understated, and its use in this way happens to be concentrated in a few areas). To get the true picture on engineer performance, investigation in-depth on a case by case basis is necessary, but the resources for doing this may not be available.

Frequency of control

In a mature market, frequent control may be used, since the service process will be well understood and progress can be reviewed according to well-known criteria. This stability should also encourage automation of the control process. In an immature environment, frequent review for control purposes may damage morale, although in such situations companies tend to want to control more, not less. In this case, control by exception may be better (i.e. invoking control only if performance or productivity depart from target by a specified amount - either overall or for specific products, areas, etc.). The frequency and nature of control have important implications for organisation structure (number of levels and spans of control).

CONTROL VIA AUDIT

Occasionally, comprehensive control is required, to ensure that service strategies, policy, structure and performance are in tune with overall company objectives and with the business environment. This consists of a comprehensive examination of every aspect of service from almost every conceivable service perspective. Such an examination is only occasionally needed where prices, products, technology, reliability, competition and company objectives are relatively stable. Where such stability does not exist, an audit may be required as frequently as once every two or three years. The checklists at the end of each chapter of this book may serve as the basis for such an audit.

Problems in initiating audits

The companies most in need of an audit are often those where service managers feel they have least time to examine all aspects of policy. They are often preoccupied with firefighting, on problems which would not have occurred if they had revised their approach on the basis of an audit. In such cases, the need for an audit may be signalled by general management, or by others with a more general responsibility (e.g. corporate planning, finance). However, if this is the route by which an audit is initiated, there may be problems in getting the audit accepted by service management - it may be seen as opening the door for outsiders to dig into the service operation. So, if service management is reluctant to embark upon an audit when one seems to be needed, some way must be found of getting that management to come round to suggesting the audit themselves. In this way, all the positive motivational factors that operate in situations like this will be harnessed by the service arm's ownership of the audit. It will improve their involvement, and their contribution to the direction of the audit. It will also increase the likelihood of their learning from the audit and reduce resistance to solutions suggested by it.

No panacea

An audit is not a panacea for all ills. It will tend to show problems that are obvious to some managers, but not to all. It spotlights problems and neglected opportunities against the background of the total business and company situation, enabling senior managers to see more clearly the costs imposed and the opportunities foregone by not improving. It also encourages management to revisit their basic assumptions about the role of service in the company.

An audit can be carried out with varying degrees of specificity. It may focus on a single policy area (e.g. servicing a particular group of customers), but audit of one policy area typically shows the need for all areas to be investigated, since what is done in one area is often the result of the same policy process, set of decisions or management style that determines what is done in all areas.

CHECKLIST FOR CHAPTER 12

Productivity

* Are our productivity measures varied enough, given the variety of inputs used and outputs delivered by our service operation?
* Do the measures used include level of service, financial, semi-financial and physical measures?
* Do they include input-input and output-output measures?
* Do we tie our measures of productivity to adding value to customers?
* Do we select, from the various productivity measures used to understand and plan the service operation, a small subset of measures for controlling the operation?
* Does this subset bear a clear relation to the job objectives of those staff whose activities are controlled by them?
* Do our productivity objectives keep in balance the short and long term objectives of the service operation?
* Do we use productivity measures for short term resource optimisation?
* Have we considered the advantages and disadvantages of allocating responsibility for productivity to central authority or to local units?
* Have we considered a variety of types of productivity schemes?
* Do our criteria for choice between productivity schemes relate closely to the management style of our operation, and the skills and motivation of all our staff?
* Have we attempted to measure and control management productivity?

Planning, targeting and control

* Have we considered the advantages of different approaches to planning (top-down, bottom-up, hybrid)?
* Does our planning approach take into account the skills and motivation of all our staff, the financial needs of the company, and the degree of flexibility needed given the business and technical environment?
* Is our planning system flexible enough to allow local variations to targets according to local needs?
* Is our budgeting system distinct enough from planning and targeting systems for the latter to be used to change and motivate the business?
* Do our analyses of performance against target allow us to distinguish clearly between individual and policy successes and failures?

* Is the frequency with which we take control actions throughout the service organisation consistent with the degree of responsibility and motivation which we want to exist in the organisation?
* Have we considered a regular service audit (in individual units of the organisation or throughout the organisation)?

13 ORGANISING FOR CUSTOMER SERVICE

There are two main ways of organising for customer service:

1. As a separate activity, with its own operating and financial targets and organisational hierarchy.
2. As an integral part of the relationship with customers, including sales, after-sales support and supplies. Service is integrated at local level, with technical aspects supported by specialist staff at various levels.

The trend is towards the first solution, mainly because separating activities leads to better control over profits and costs. This solution is also adopted because sales and marketing staff may regard service either as a necessary evil, a fixed cost, or as a limitless resource to help them make sales. Typically, service prices are discounted to ease equipment sale, with no awareness of the consequences for profit margins.

From a marketing perspective, the first is a second-best solution, adopted because of the inability of management to find effective ways of managing an integrated interface with the customer. Unless the customer distinguishes clearly and absolutely between sales, service, support and so on, functional separation usually causes communication problems and lost marketing opportunities. At worst, it can lead to permanent battle lines drawn between sales and service functions.

Yet it can be very difficult to manage field service together with sales operations. Service needs technical and logistic back- up services which are more readily available within a close vertically integrated service department than from a central staff support operation. However, some computer companies are finding that as the importance of software sales and support increases, the neat dividing line between the skills and management processes required for sales and support disappears.

A compromise is to adopt a matrix solution, where service exists both as a function and as part of the integrated local team. The communication and management problems of matrix organisations are well known. Matrix organisation requires managers with broad perspectives. There must be clear decision rules to cope with most cases. This applies particularly to situations in which short term goals of one dimension of the matrix (e.g. the area) conflict with longer term goals of another (e.g. service). Conflicting issues must be resolved by reference to a common goal, such as profit. If responsibility for profit is not delegated, matrix organisations are very difficult to manage. There is a risk of strong local management evolving, without the appropriate financial controls.

REPORTING RELATIONSHIPS

In the classic branch service organisation, service management control operations in branches, including local technical, work control, inventory and costing departments. Special expertise in technical and inventory support is used in an advisory way at local level and provides central back-up for the field. This structure may be more effective if operated via control systems which give local profit responsibility.

In more centralised operations, support expertise is used more directly. Centralised departments control technical and inventory operations. Call receipt is located where it can be most economic. This structure requires the targets for each manager to be set carefully so that they are relevant and acceptable to him. Otherwise motivation may suffer.

The management style of the company and the breadth and technical complexity of its product range affects choice of structure. If the product range is very wide, and different areas differ significantly in their requirements, the first structure is more appropriate. If the product range is narrow, and the level of service standard across the country, the second kind of structure is more appropriate. In general, the choice between centralised or devolved structures is a choice between application of concentrated skills and expertise via a centralised system, and the strengths of local understanding, authority, control and motivation. Company structure should give the best compromise between the two, taking into account the skills and abilities of the current service management team.

In the computing industry, decentralisation of hardware maintenance is often accompanied by centralisation of hardware support and of software maintenance and support. The latter seems to be more amenable to central organisation, as it does not require physical replacement. There are, however, strong arguments for decentralised support (whether of hardware - where support is also being centralised - or software) particularly those relating to ease of contact, and flexibility of response to variations in customer requirements.

Service as a profit centre

Many companies run field service as a profit centre, using modern information systems to make high quality financial data available to field service. Service may be set up as a profit centre (or as a separate company) to protect it from extreme fluctuations in the sales side of the business. This is more common in companies operating in rapidly developing, competitive and uncertain markets (e.g. microcomputers). Another reason is to enable service to capture additional service revenue (e.g. third party) with less confusion on overall company objectives. The key issue here is whether overall marketing and customer care objectives are also taken into account.

Under the profit centre concept, some aspects of service (e.g. special support staff) may be more centralised, due to improvements in communications. Other aspects may be more decentralised (e.g. decisions on priorities between customers, on parts usage). This may result in lower costs, quicker response and increased customer satisfaction (provided profit objectives have a major long-term component). Managers also have the incentive to make changes which result in increased revenue, rather than operating solely by tight cost budgets. Other benefits include increased status for the service organisation, improved cost discipline, greater attention to the revenue consequences of actions, and a more business-like orientation. The concept can lead to greater concentration on adding value to the customer and on keeping the customer.

LINE STRUCTURE

Assuming that service is treated as a separate function, we now consider where line and support functions should be. For a small service organisation, there is little doubt about the organisational location of line functions. There may be just one national service manager and his engineers! In larger companies, the local service manager usually reports to a national service manager, but some companies have one, two or even three more tiers in the organisation. It is hard to understand what some of these managers do, except pass information up and down! Such multi-tiered hierarchies are the result of unwillingness of top management to delegate, or absence of efficiency pressure, combined with job analysis not identifying what tasks are really necessary.

Organisation of engineers

The physical location of engineers is a critical question. If they share one location, then they will be busy almost 100% of the time because the total service workload can be spread amongst the engineers. However, travelling time may be astronomical, while response time targets may often be missed. Only the smallest companies can work successfully like this.

At the other extreme engineers can be located individually throughout the country, each with his own area. This gives rapid response to many of the calls, but can be wasteful of engineer time. Each engineer will only have a small population of customers to deal with. Breakdowns are random - at times there will be no calls, at other times several calls within a short space of time, when the engineer will have to call for help or make the customer wait. The local engineer also has to be able to repair any type of equipment on his patch, while the central engineer can be a specialist.

Most locational decisions are a compromise between these two situations, depending on factors such as:
- Required response times.
- Travel time.
- Resulting productive proportion of engineer time.
- Variety of equipment.
- Range of engineer skills.
- Dispersion of installed base.
- Cost of running local branches.
- Economics and speed of spares support.

Supervision of engineers

The economics of field service are a difficult balance between tight control with high overheads, and slack control with high direct costs. Occasionally, companies manage to cut through this Gordian knot, by creating a high level of motivation amongst engineers, and decentralising key targets. The first line manager must therefore be able to :

- Maintain tight overall control relating to key targets.
- Use a minimum of feedback to maintain control.
- Motivate engineers.
- Take a rounded business approach to service.

If line managers are not able to do this, companies tend to use a large management team to control and monitor the situation, raising overhead costs.

Spans of control

There are a large number of theoretical works on this general subject. They suggest that a supervisor is best when he has up to 5 subordinates, and becomes ineffective with more than 8. Generally in manufacturing industry the line supervisor controls between 11 and 24 operatives. The service manager is in a similar position to the manufacturing supervisor in that engineers often work in teams and senior team members can help to supervise.

Our work shows that first line service managers have between 10 and 40 engineers each. The wide variation is due to the organisation of engineers into teams. Where the manager is responsible for individual engineers or for small teams then he will have less than 20 engineers, normally about 14. Where there are working team leaders, the manager reduces the effective numbers reporting to him by some delegation.

Where several engineers work for a team leader, teams consist of between 6 and 14 people. Engineers work in groups of 6 to 16, controlled by supervisors who are administrators at least part time. Within this structure there may be small groups who work together and contribute in small ways to job control and reporting. The idea of working team organisers is attractive because it can save supervisory manpower. However, there are problems in communicating with a leader who is out making calls much of the time. The manpower saving may not be quite what it appears to be, either. An average manager with 3 team leaders is likely to have 30 engineers. If the leaders spend 25% of their time on organising, only a quarter of a man is saved over having 2 managers each directly looking after 15 engineers. If the leaders spend 50% of their time in supervision, then they cost the company an extra half man. So the economic argument is not clear cut. The benefits of either structure should take into account the following:

- Since engineers do confer over technical matters there is no significant extra time spent if a senior engineer becomes a team leader.
- Some team leaders tend to make administration a full time job.
- Managers freed from daily details can run more effective branches.
- Communications with travelling team organisers can be poor.
- The existence of team leader grade for senior engineers may be seen as a career path and improve engineer morale.

Manpower planning

As most service costs are related to manpower, it is critical that the correct number of engineers is available to give the required service. With too few engineers, support obligations will not be met. With too many, costs will be high and customers will look elsewhere for support and eventually for equipment. Correct manning levels are therefore essential. In this section, we summarise the main determinants of manning levels.

Engineer utilisation

Most companies use their engineers primarily on breakdowns. Engineer time is often split equally between breakdown repair and travelling, with other activities taking a minor but still significant portion. However, a small amount of planned maintenance appears to improve service performance. One method of organising planned maintenance is to have a special team with different expertise to carry out the operation. Alternatively, all engineers may do planned maintenance, reducing any troughs in the workload.

Call rate

The call rate depends on travel time, which in turn depends principally on the relatively fixed factor of equipment distribution, and the variable factors of failure distribution and service time.

Equipment distribution, serviceability and reliability

The installed-base density, reliability and serviceability of equipment of different types may determine how we organise the range serviced by each engineer and how we train him. Where there are many machines of each type, where calls are very frequent, or where each piece of equipment takes a long time to service, an engineer can specialise on a narrow product range. Where particular equipment types are rare or rarely need servicing, local engineers need wider training to look after them (though if they are easy to service, this is not a problem). Specialisation is not an economic option. Where the total equipment population is low or reliability very high, there is either poor engineer utilisation or high travelling time. A versatile engineering force is needed here. However serviceable the machine, failure in inventory management may reduce engineer utilisation by increasing time spent waiting for parts. In some sectors this problem will be reduced by use of remote diagnostics and exchange modules.

Response time
This determines the number of surplus engineers required to guarantee maintaining customer service levels. If response time is very short, engineers must be free to react as soon as the fault is reported. If the customer accepts slower service, the engineers' workload can be planned to minimise both travel and waiting time.

Number of machines per engineer
When all the above factors are taken into account, the demand for engineering time can be calculated. Because of the complex nature of interaction between these factors and their probabilistic nature, the best way of doing this before product launch is by computer simulation. After launch, statistics on the demand for calls become available, and real life customer behaviour also emerges. This enables initial manpower estimates to be improved.

ENGINEER SKILLS
In many sectors, a number of changes are occurring which put at issue the required skill level of travelling engineers. These include:
- Lack of skilled engineers.
- Increasing use of modular and change-board design.
- Development of equipment with diagnostics.
- Cost of employing and equipping a skilled man.
- Less opportunity to use skill on-site in making inventive repairs.
- Pressure to make efficient use of time via rapid repair rather than solving the problem.

Table 13.1 Engineer skill levels

GRADE OF SKILL	%
Unskilled	1
Low skilled	2
Skilled	83
Technologists	14

Many companies are attempting to simplify repairs, to reduce the need for skilled engineers. However, actual skill levels are changing slowly. In Table 13.1, we show the distribution of engineer skills, measured by the number of people in each category, taken from our survey of companies in the computer and electronic equipment sectors. It shows that most engineers are the traditional skilled variety. This may seem surprising, given the dramatic changes that are occurring in the approach to field service. However, most companies' need to maintain a substantial population of obsolescent equipment.

The complexity and serviceability of equipment determines skill levels needed. If different skill levels are needed, this may be achieved through a structure which grades engineers by skill. This also gives the individual a route to supervisory status, subject to the qualification that ability to progress to higher skill levels may not indicate managerial ability.

TRAINING
The main elements of engineer training are:
- All major components, their identification, location, purpose and relation to other components.
- Tracing of appropriate connections, circuits and flows.
- Diagnosis of expected problems, related components, their repair and replacement.
- Safety features, safeguards, their purpose, effectiveness and checking.

- Wider product knowledge (typical use situations, customer benefits, customers).
- Service procedures and processes.
- Testing and certification of the trained engineer.
- Up-dating of training (school, bulletins), testing and certification.
- Passing on 'short cuts' discovered after product launch (e.g. via bulletins, service meetings).
- Retraining to handle additional modules, new products, etc.
- Customer care and the engineer's role in keeping the customer.

Additional training for managers might cover:
- Management problem diagnosis.
- Staff training (technical and customer care).
- Administrative skills.
- Customer relations.
- Hiring, dismissal and employee relations.

Junior engineers may also need more general industry background training. However a large amount of time spent in training sessions results in a worse call rate. Too little time results in poorer or longer fixes. Careful matching of skill levels to equipment complexity and serviceability should allow companies to reduce wasted training time.

In some sectors many calls result from trivial causes, such as dirt, operator error, or poor adjustment. In such cases, engineers need no great knowledge of the equipment, but a basic understanding of how it works and ways to rectify simple faults. If the majority of engineer calls are of this type, then having well qualified engineers with specific product skills is less advantageous.

Larger companies tend to do the bulk of the training, with smaller companies 'poaching' trained engineers. With so many engineers, larger companies can organise by expertise or location. They tend to promote staff from simpler to more complex machines. This creates a dilemma. To work effectively, engineers need to be taught more about how equipment operates. This will enable them to repair subsequent versions of the equipment, but may be less effective in the short term than detailed training on repair of the current model. Since smaller companies depend upon larger ones for trained personnel, good basic training may not be in the interest of larger companies. It is in the small companies, where the engineer has to apply his basic knowledge to more varied situations, that this kind of training is more useful.

Third party maintenance training

Many equipment suppliers are not keen to provide new product technical information to third party maintenance suppliers, whose engineers may therefore have no opportunity to gain in-depth equipment knowledge except via on the job training. These companies usually service a wide range of equipment, with each engineer servicing all the machines in his area. For this reason, it has taken some time for third party maintenance companies to reach respectability. Some operators attempt to provide everything, charge little, and achieve even less. At the same time more reputable companies provide a service comparable with the original equipment suppliers. Many third party maintenance companies rely on recruiting trained engineers from companies who make the equipment they service.

MOTIVATING ENGINEERS

Better engineer motivation improves customer satisfaction and productivity. So can incentives be used to improve motivation? Some companies apply the monetary incentive model used in their sales force, and find this backfires, as some engineers regard it as an insult to their professionalism. In other companies, these incentives work well. Incentives work best when closely tied to objectives which an engineer connects with his own success (e.g. service revenue, customer satisfaction). Much may depend upon the seniority of the engineer, the training and incentives used in the past, and how any incentive programme is introduced (e.g. as a nice prize, or as a desperate attempt to bolster customer satisfaction). A central requirement is that any such programme must be properly communicated (sold?) to engineers.

The factors which damage motivation include:
- Poor equipment documentation.
- Too much paperwork.
- Badly designed equipment.
- Too much pressure to repair too quickly.
- Failure to provide test equipment of the right quality.
- Spares shortages.

- Reduction in skills required.
- Failure to structure jobs to provide interest and challenge.
- Failure to provide a clear and interesting career path.
- Failure to maintain image of company in the market.
- Failure to train adequately.
- Absence of secure and pleasant work environment (e.g. working from home).
- Failure to understand management and man management.

SUPPORT STRUCTURE

Service needs to be supported by functions such as:
- Design and technical.
- Repair centre.
- Distribution.
- Spare parts.

Design and technical

Design and technical support for engineers is often provided by a central technical team. They may have some role in equipment development, but in larger companies tend to be specialists (often working at national or international level) in modifying equipment for field operations and providing service documentation. The design team is more likely to be located in the manufacturing organisation or in a specialist development function, and not easily accessible to service operations, except when there is a major problem.

Local technical experts tend to deal with a variety of equipment, while central technicians tend to advise on a narrow range, and are therefore likely to solve specific problems better. The local expert can visit sites easily, to implement solutions on the spot. This can encourage slack practices in documentation and exceptional repair procedures. Further, when he is on site he may not be available for other enquiries. He may be tempted to resolve the problem rather than giving the engineer the satisfaction of making the repair.

Improved communications and remote diagnosis are reinforcing the tendency to centralise technical support in some sectors, particularly for products with a strong software element. The support may be direct to the customer, in the form of a 'hot line'. The skills required to solve less common problems may be in such short supply that the company has no option but to centralise support.

Repair centre

The repair centre may be an extension of the field engineers' own activities, a separate division, part of manufacturing, or part of a separate spare parts operation. Each arrangement has its strengths and weaknesses. Integration with manufacturing usually implies good availability of components and skilled labour, observance of production disciplines and good test facilities. However, repair jobs do not often come through in the large batches which the factory likes, and they do not give the same turnover as products. The time taken to repair modules by this method can be months, which is inconsistent with efficient spares supply. Further, many of the items being repaired may be obsolete, needing special parts and possibly special procedures.

These factors lead some companies to set up separate repair centres. If this is done on a large enough scale (often international), efficiency is usually better than if repair were a factory responsibility. There is a constant flow of repairs coming in and engineers are experienced in common faults and make rapid repairs. The time taken to return equipment and parts is usually shorter than for manufacturing, but there may be more difficulty in obtaining the parts needed to complete repairs. There may also be a cost problem, especially if many items are returned for checking rather than with identified faults.

Control of repairs within the local service operation helps balance engineer workload. It ensures that engineers are capable of carrying out fundamental repairs rather than simply exchanging modules. However, repair control may be weak. If engineers repair parts locally, repair methods may differ between areas. Unless the inventory control system incorporates locally repaired items, there may be imbalances between areas, with some areas ordering parts which are in surplus elsewhere. With the high price of test equipment, the best diagnostics may not be available in each branch, and the quality of repair may be low and inconsistent.

The centre may carry out various functions, including remanufacturing, testing, repair of equipment serviced on a 'bring-in' basis, and module or part repairs. Repair centres may complicate the supply of parts to the field, particularly if repairable modules are used. If the number of repairable modules available is fixed, they must be recycled quickly, or else there may be frequent shortages and emergency orders on the repair centre. If repairable parts are over-ordered, inventory may be inflated for some time.

If the repair centre is controlled by the local service branch, the risks are:
   - Priorities are changed too often, resulting in inefficiency.
   - Parts usage is not identified, giving field shortages & excess stocks.

Local or central repair
The choice of local or central repair often depends on the cost of test equipment and the design of modules. If test equipment is relatively inexpensive, repairs can be done locally. This is an advantage where modules are mainly used for test purposes and the proportion that fail is low.

A common cause of local repair is the unreliability of supply of repaired modules. The situation can become progressively worse if not controlled properly. When return from the repair centre is poor, engineers tend to keep defective modules in case they will work or can be repaired locally. This reduces availability of modules for repair and increases unreliability of supply from the the repair centre. An engineer can then justify his action of withholding the return of the module! This leads to a long cycle time for return of defective modules once they have been removed from equipment. To avoid this problem, strong centralised control is used by many companies in allocation and return of repairable modules. Even where there is local repair, the state and location of all high value modules is controlled from a support group.

Repairable modules
While repairable modules provide many opportunities for increasing efficiency, they pose some problems for organising service (apart from the obvious ones of who owns the exchanged module and whether the customer perceives it to be a second hand part!). The major issues are
   - Who should make the repair?
   - Where should it be done?
If repair involves specialised equipment or test facilities which are uneconomical to site in every service branch, either the manufacturing function carries out the repair, or service centres may be needed. If the latter, should it be staffed by

engineers who also make field service calls? The advantages of engineers carrying out off-site repair of modules are:
- Speed of repair.
- The engineer is well acquainted with the symptoms of failure.
- Cost of repair is low.
- Unwanted modules are not repaired.

The disadvantages are:
- Test procedures are less rigorous.
- Quality of repair is less consistent.
- Poor control of repair history.
- Less recording of failure modes.
- Poor distribution priorities.

Printed circuit boards (PCBs) provide an interesting case. As they often have a high value, the company aims to keep the stock to a minimum. Most companies do not allow their engineers to carry out local repairs to any extent. Some carry out local sorting of PCBs which appear to have no fault, often because a PCB was used for diagnosis purposes and the original PCB was left in the equipment. There is no evidence that it is defective, and it can be used again for diagnostic purposes with little risk of it being faulty, so long as it has been tested at the local branch.

PCBs are often returned to a central repair workshop where they undergo full testing and repair. In some companies the moving and repair of PCBs is a protracted affair and leads to shortages and repair problems. This repair facility is normally not included in the service operations of large companies, perhaps because workshop repair is seen as manufacturing, since it uses the same components and often requires the same type of test equipment. Usually repair times and parts availability are poor. Equipment manufacture takes precedence over parts in the use of resources.

Parts distribution

The service organisation is very dependent on this function. It may be a separate department, part of factory operations, or controlled by marketing via equipment distribution. Improved communications and more professional distribution management have made this area less problematic than formerly. Good inventory and service planning should allow the company to run a rational and cost effective distribution system, with a clear link between the rapidity of response required and distribution methods and costs. In all systems there are emergencies where speed of delivery is crucial, irrespective of cost. This calls for some flexibility in system capacity, and may necessitate the use of outside contractors.

Spare parts

Spare parts supply from source to engineer may be organised as part of the service operation, as a separate function, as part of a physical distribution function, or as an extension of manufacturing inventory operations. The main purpose of this function is to support service, so the service function should control this operation, provided appropriate financial targets are adopted (e.g. return on assets).

In spares support there are four tasks to be covered:

- Local stock control.
- Central stores management.
- Inventory level control.
- Purchasing.

Each of these tasks may be carried out by different departments, e.g.

Local stock control	Branch service
Central stores management	Logistic support group
Inventory level control	Technical support group
Purchasing	Company purchasing department

This structure may lead to high stock (due to stock-to-stock transactions), long supply lead times, and poor customer service. There is also a group trying to control the inventory level which has no direct authority for the results. This situation can be improved by the following arrangement:

Let us examine how each department would work under this system.

Local stock control	Local service management
Central stores management	Inventory support
Inventory level control	Inventory support
Purchasing	Spares purchasing

Local service management would be responsible for physical storekeeping within branch stores. This should lead to good control over supply and return of parts between store and engineer. The local storeman maintains stock levels as directed by inventory support personnel. The amount of stock and its value are set centrally because local management are likely to hold excess stock.

Central stores management controls warehouse stock and arranges distribution to branches. Their physical movement records provide information used in inventory level control, in assessing the correct amount of stock to be held at each location. For new products, central stores management identify requirements and link directly to purchasing.

Inventory level control is a back-up staff task, based on analytical techniques and equipment knowledge. Much of the work may be devoted to supporting new products. The assessment of the target level for any part is a continuous exercise. Equipment population, usage rates, and repair methods change, affecting the quantity needed. For proper inventory balance, target levels should be continually reset. The system for resetting inventory targets may be adapted to monitor actual inventory levels as well. This may also ensure that the targets are realistic, while inventory controllers allocate available inventory when plans go awry. This may involve having central control personnel who maintain the optimum spares level throughout the country, turning the task from a support task into a line one.

Purchasing is normally via a central purchasing function. Given the number and variety of spares items, the purchasing function allocate specialists for different items. Much purchasing is for simple repeat items, involving placing orders and monitoring delivery. Where central stores are responsible for reordering, purchasing may have to review order quantities against inventory level control targets. The ordering process varies with stock policy, with some items being ordered according to forecast demand, and others (typically slow moving) being ordered as and when inventory falls below a certain level. Purchasing officers may want to exercise discretion in batching of orders for suppliers who supply more than one part, to save delivery and administrative charges. However, this can cause problems of availability, so it should be made clear where discretion is allowed. Good forecasting and delivery scheduling may help to optimise multi-part order size and parts availability.

Inventory support departments may be merged into a composite operation. The support manager, reporting probably to the service director, handles all spare parts inventory functions. The key personnel are inventory level controllers, who identify correct parts levels and control against these levels. Inventory specialists are supplied with product technical information from the technical support department. If parts are reordered routinely from suppliers, this may be done by the inventory level controllers as well. Purchasing are concerned with prices and the search for alternative suppliers or special parts. Central and local storemen work for the support manager, with some responsibility for supplying local demand factors to inventory control. The support manager may have responsibility for logistic support, including transport.

Call receipt function

We have already considered the organisation of call receipt (p.143). Having a call receiver in each branch means that the individual in question may reflect the local image of the company, work closely with engineers and managers, and perhaps get to know the customer. The price is having many people doing a job which could be handled centrally by fewer staff.

SUPPORT RATIOS

How much support (e.g. call receipt, work control, stores, technical support, repair centre) do engineers need to keep working efficiently? Our work suggests that besides a line manager per 12 engineers, the average is one member of support staff per 5 engineers. This may appear to be a large number of non-productive staff, but their role is to ensure that the right engineer gets to the right customer, fast, with the right spares, and is capable of repairing the equipment.

The location of support staff is a matter for compromise, as we have already noted. Local technical support enables customers to be visited and helped, but if support is centralised, staff are fewer and more highly qualified. Similar arguments apply to call receipt, parts control, and other services. The better commitment, local knowledge, and availability of local support personnel must be set against the greater expertise, fewer staff and a wider view of opportunities and problems of central support.

With over 2 back-up staff per manager in most companies, their contribution to achieving service objectives must be rigorously analysed. There is scope for rationalisation in many companies, particularly multinationals, which seem prone to duplication of effort and overmanning. This can be seen particularly between international and national levels, with international staff designing schemes which are brilliant conceptually, but have little chance of working in the field. Mistrust often builds up, and the national entity tends not to accept the advice and information provided. In the worst cases, perfectly sensible schemes are put to local service managers who decide according to their 'feel', a subjective assessment which is unlikely to be very good. But the ability of staff remote from operations to understand operating conditions is always questionable. Good communication can show where problems can be avoided, and help to remove possible conflicts.

CHECKLIST FOR CHAPTER 13

Relationship with other functions

* If the service operation has total responsibility for profit and customer satisfaction, is there a process by which the effect of other functions on these objectives can be controlled or influenced?
* Have we considered strengths and weaknesses of merging responsibility for customer sales and service at local levels, with service and marketing acting as staff functions, or intermediate matrix solutions?
* If service is a profit centre, what steps have we taken to ensure that customer satisfaction objectives are not overridden by profit objectives?
* Have we ensured that managers understand that profit can be improved by increasing revenue relative to cost, not just by cutting cost?

Internal organisation

* Does the degree of centralisation of management and support reflect the degree of variation in customer needs and equipment populations between different operating units, the economies of centralisation, and the motivational advantages of local decision-making authority?
* Do we periodically re-examine our organisation structure, to ensure that we have no redundant levels or elements, which add no value to the management process?
* Do we have a model for deciding engineer allocation (to particular areas or types of equipment), taking into account required response times, travel times, productive times, equipment variety, engineer skills, dispersion of installed base, cost of running local branches, and spares support parameters?
* Is our first line span of control wide enough to be economic, and narrow enough to allow for adequate supervision, given the nature of our engineering staff and the complexity of the service task?
* Have we considered using working supervisors to improve the cost-effectiveness of supervision?
* Does our specialist support structure (spare parts, technical help, etc.) ensure that responsibility for achievement is clearly allocated to particular individuals?
* Have we evolved measures of control for support staff which relate directly to our service objectives?

* Do these measures enable us to detect where waste of resources or redundancy exist?

Training
* Do we review our training needs regularly, to see whether our engineers and managers are being trained to deal with changing service tasks and customers needs?
* Are we exploiting recent changes in educational technology to optimise the effectiveness and efficiency of our training?

Motivation
* Do we recognise the importance of high levels of engineer motivation in achieving customer satisfaction, in efficient working and in avoiding work force attrition?
* Do we regularly examine all aspects of the engineer's working context to identify which factors may be leading to problems with motivation?
* Do we (as far as is possible) take prompt steps to deal with these problems?

14 INCREASING PRODUCTIVITY AND PROFIT

Electronics has increased the reliability of many kinds of equipment. In some cases this coincided with rapid growth in the installed base. Electronics has also been used to increase the complexity (hardware or software) of equipment. This means that the demand for service staff has not fallen as might have been expected. The result has been a shortage of engineers in some sectors, while there has been a surplus in others. In some markets pressure on service prices has increased. These factors combined have intensified the search for ways of increasing service productivity.

In sectors where there has been a surplus of engineers, the situation has been aggravated by low staff turnover. In the long run, such problems may be soluble via lower paid, part-time or contract staff. In the short run, costs may be saved by moving in the opposite direction, by widening the range of tasks carried out by engineers, to include those currently carried out by contractors or by groups subject to higher staff turnover rates (delivery, sales). If engineers have to be provided with transport, then mobile tasks are prime candidates for merging of roles. Profit orientation normally goes a long way to forcing resolution of such issues.

This chapter examines some of the main opportunities for service organisations to increase profit with least risk to customer satisfaction. A more comprehensive listing would include:
- More clear and/or aggressive service profit goals.
- Improved service market segmentation.
- Greater use of the full marketing mix in marketing service.
- Delegating responsibility to lower levels.
- Better use of management information to identify profit opportunities.
- Automating call response systems.
- Improved testing procedures.
- Remote diagnostics.
- Improved maintainability of products (e.g. modularity).
- Reduced and/or regionalised spare parts inventory.
- Regional resource centres.

- Regional work control centres.
- Use of modern technology to improve communication with engineers.
- Low cost service centres.
- Lower cost but better training (often in-branch, not central).
- Reduction of number of management levels.
- Reduction of number of sites or amount of facilities.
- Working team managers.
- Management by exception.
- Improved harnessing of engineer motivation (team bonuses, etc.).

A MORE EFFECTIVE ORGANISATION

A slimmer organisation may be more profitable. The number of levels of organisation and spans of control affect costs and performance, as follows:
- The organisation's cost may put service costs above competitive levels.
- The structure may have a counterproductive effect on business. Too wide a span of control may mean ineffective supervision. Too narrow a span may lead to high costs and over-supervision. Too few levels of organisation may lead to too much data reaching top management, who are unable to make sense of what is happening. Too many leads to high overhead costs, over-supervision or too much activity devoted to reporting and control.

Organisational cost

One sign of trouble is an over-rich manpower support structure. There may be too many levels (with each level partly duplicating the functions of levels above and below), or support manpower may have responsibilities normally allocated to line management. This situation may emerge in years of plenty, and be noticed only in years of famine. What may be needed is a zero-base approach to levels of organisation and support staff, with the question being 'Why should not certain tasks be allocated to line managers or engineers or else be condensed with a number of other tasks into a single job?'

In some larger companies, a rich support structure may indicate that much support manpower is not devoted to aiding performance, but to reporting or analysis. This may be redundant, as today it can be automated by good data base design, programming and communication techniques.

Manageable units in service

One way to reduce costs may be to reduce field service to manageable units, i.e. the size of unit to which broad business responsibilities (profit, cost, level of service and customer satisfaction) can be allocated, harnessing motivation to improve performance, while reducing costs, over-division of labour, and the need for detailed control. The risk is that each unit develops an overhead structure. This has to be dealt with by strict profit targetting.

Key ratios in the organisation

In smaller service organisations, the first line span of control may be based on time allocation, with engineers and managers having duties which are not strictly related to performing or managing field service. Engineers may have a selling role (particularly if they are working from a sales outlet), while managers may either have responsibilities in other areas, or may be part-time engineers themselves. Engineers may carry out some parts/module repair or remanufacturing, though here the span of control may not be affected, since the manager in charge of service is usually in charge of such activities. If there is no full time service manager (e.g. small dealers), management control may be by the owner or overall manager. In medium-sized service organisations, there will normally be one, or at most two, levels of service management (typically engineers reporting to a service manager or technical manager, or reporting to area service managers who report to the general service manager).

For larger companies, with two or more management tiers, a key measure is the ratio of line managers to engineers, or total line span of control. This span may be reduced in large service organisations by adding further hierarchies. The justification for this is increased efficiency, normally through economies of scale. Larger service organisations tend to serve a more dense equipment base and should have lower travel times. Unless the variety of equipment has increased with the size of the base, engineers specialisation will cut repair times. If there are no economies of scale (often the case), other solutions may have to be found. These include more self-management in local service branches, enabling the next layer up to manage with a wider span of control.

Support staff

Support staff may specialise in administration, work control, call receipt, or handling complaints. This is 'line administrative support'. Or they may be technical, dedicated to helping engineers out with problems. This is 'line technical support'. In addition to line management overhead, there is also indirect support overhead - typically technical specialists who devise service procedures, headquarters service staff who devise service policies and help administer the service operation, and non-direct clerical staff. These are "staff support". Our studies show that the (quite large) variations in all span measures (line management, line support, and staff support) are often not related to complexity of equipment or geographical factors.

Reducing redundant support

As efficiency pressures increase on service organisations, one cost cutting option is reducing staff support, whether in headquarters, regional or local offices. Much of this staff may have been justified in the past by the complexity of a service operation dealing with relatively unreliable equipment. Line administrative support may also be reduceable, since its level may have been determined by what was required when communications, work allocation and diagnostic systems were relatively basic. Line administration can be partially automated by remote diagnosis, although there is still some need for a human interface. As service parameters change, there is a clear need for a zero-base audit of staff support or, optimally, an attempt to predict staff support requirements on a realistic basis. One problem is that those who make service policy are the very people whose jobs might be threatened by the results of such an audit.

In large operations line support (administrative or technical) can be reduced by pushing it up one more level in the hierarchy (from local to regional, regional to national). Better qualified staff may be employed for more complex products, but customer satisfaction may suffer. One solution is to have service administration (call handling, despatch of technical specialists) carried out more centrally, but retain the local service structure physically, so that call-backs in connection with a specific job can be handled locally.

Working team organisers

Our studies show that companies with working team organisers have double the nominal first line span of control of those that do not. Obtaining the full benefits of this system depends entirely on the effectiveness of the team organisers in combining supervision and servicing. An advantage of this system is that much other line support and management is related to the number of first line managers, not the number of engineers. So this system, if it can be worked effectively, may cut most staff overheads in two.

THE COST OF THE ENGINEER
Time allocation
There are various ways to improve engineer utilisation without prejudicing other service objectives. One way, planned maintenance, demands better methods of locating and communicating with the engineer in customer premises, to pull him off planned maintenance for emergencies (e.g. with bleepers - also useful for working organisers), and different work control practices to provide last-minute scheduling of optimum machines for planned maintenance (e.g. according to customer priority or location of last call).

Salaries
With many service organisations under pressure on costs, salaries paid may not be justified by maintenance revenue. For larger companies, the situation is aggravated by slow turnover amongst engineers (normally the most stable workforce). A change in skill structures takes time to implement if the company wants to avoid labour trouble. Many companies may use tiered solutions, with the employment of lower skilled/paid staff for simpler tasks (routine maintenance). Another solution is to treat some engineers as an asset in serving the customer base, and devise marketing or quasi-marketing tasks for them. Note that high salary levels affect most adversely those companies which are least effective in their use of service manpower.

SERVICE CENTRES
Some companies which formerly operated solely via a direct, calling service force are using service centres (SCs) usually consisting of a site to which equipment can be brought by customers or engineers for repair or module swap. If equipment is portable, SCs can bring big cost savings without cutting service levels. The benefits are normally reduced non-parts costs, especially increased net engineer working hours (time previously spent waiting can be used on servicing machines brought in, or returned loaner machines), and reduced travel, car/van depreciation, employment costs, and overheads. Benefits may come from lower inventory holding costs (reduction in van kits)

and reliability (bench testing in SCs). SC job costs are dominated by pick-up, redelivery and loan machines.

Who brings the equipment in?

The bring-in opportunity offers the chance of lower price incentives to the buyer to bring-in. This can also be applied to bringing equipment to sales locations as well as SCs, with transport of machines to SCs as part of the regular physical distribution system. This applies especially to companies selling through retail or dealer locations, but retaining total or partial service. It reduces the number of service locations necessary - transport costs are the main limiting factor. It ensures that the key contact between selling point and customer is kept alive (even though in the context of machine failure, it can be an opportunity to demonstrate customer-orientation and make a profit at the same time). If the customer does not want to bring in equipment, it may be as feasible for the salesman to do it as the engineer, and may be of greater benefit. On travel grounds the nearest person (salesman or engineer) should bring in the equipment, but this involves abandoning the sales/service division that many companies maintain.

Structural consequences

If a company moves from on-site service to SCs (for all or part of its product range), this may imply major changes for the rest of the service organisation. It would probably simplify it. For example, it may allow for substantial reduction in non-technical support staff and in the number of levels of reporting, and increase in spans of control.

Loaners

One unquantifiable but important marketing benefit of replacements or loaners is that the level of service to the customer when a loaner is provided is much greater. It may be realisable in a premium priced contract, but at the least it is a weapon in customer base protection.

Economies of scale

SCs must be large enough to reap scale economies of engineer specialisation, inventory, and administrative overhead. The span of control may be larger than in a service district (unless the latter uses the concept of the working team leader). The manager may also be servicing for some of the time.

EQUIPMENT FACTORS
Design
Many design improvements can be made to reduce service costs, such as reduced numbers of parts per machine, modularity, simplicity, customer replaceable parts, reduced customer error likelihood, and customer installable equipment. These changes may finally reduce service prices, but being behind competition on these points will put the company at risk, although good service marketing may put off the evil hour. Companies servicing too wide, old or complex a range of products incur higher service costs. However, drastic rationalisation may cause loss of market share. The trick is to create a varied range with maximum parts standardisation and ensure that products are designed and marketed to die relatively early.

Material costs
Increasing reliability should reduce the impact of material costs (parts, components, etc.) on service costs, but two factors may militate against this. The first is the tendency to increase the mark-up on materials supplied to service operations, to ensure that profit is maintained. While fewer parts are being replaced per item of equipment, they are costing more per unit. The second factor is the trend towards modular replacement, to save service labour costs. The impact of modularity will increase if modules are made for disposability rather than repair, to save manufacturing or repair labour. Companies whose materials costs are a high proportion of service costs should be aware of this risk, especially if their current level of modularity is low. One solution is off-site repair. This may be through repair centres, where cheaper labour may be employable if different types of repair occur in enough volume for specialisation to be used (generalist repairmen are more expensive). Another solution is to use engineer waiting time for parts repair - inherent in repair centres, but extensible to a travelling force.

A good repairs policy leads to higher quality parts. Responsibility for parts failure is better understood if there is a process to trace causes of failure. Engineer involvement in solving parts reliability problems and in designing parts for easy replacement or repair may improve the parts cost situation. Longer term planning would involve the division of parts into repairable and non-repairable, according to relative replacement and repair costs. These costs should be reckoned in opportunity cost terms - if service labour has to be idle for some of the time to provide a particular level of service, then its opportunity cost is zero. A true opportunity cost approach is difficult to employ if parts transfer pricing of the above- mentioned kind is used. High parts mark-ups can force service or parts organisations to do more than the optimum level of repairing.

Controlling parts usage

The tendency of engineers to hoard parts and carry out their own preventive maintenance programmes (not necessarily a bad thing if properly controlled), can cause uneconomic parts usage. Some companies control this by targeting engineers partly on parts usage, according to expected failure rates. This is fine so long as parts requirements are accurately predictable. If not, or if the engineer (or his area office) has a lot of rogue equipment, this can cause problems. Another way to control parts usage may be through field profit responsibility. If the area service manager is responsible for profit as well as for a particular level of customer satisfaction, he can use his judgement on whether to allow leeway in early parts replacement (e.g. in the case of hyper-sensitive customers).

MARKETING FACTORS
Pricing

Pricing options which share efficiency (e.g. carry-in service) or charge for real benefits (high machine availability) are needed. Carry-in service discounts are becoming more common for products which are robustly portable enough to tolerate carry-in. Call charges are worth trying, but encouraging the customer to avoid calls can cut two ways, by making him aware of the cost per call (and the possible attractiveness of non-contractual service, which the company might not have learnt to make a success of) and of the unreliability of equipment (via the number of calls billed). Necessary calls may be avoided in extreme cases, counter-productive to both customer and supplier. All this should be avoidable by good marketing. One option, if the above disadvantages are not significant, is to use the call charge combined with a lower contract price. This implies having an efficient administration of pricing options and of billing (this applies to carry-in discounts as well). If the billing (and possibly collection) is done locally (e.g. by the engineer), the whole complexion of pricing administration changes anyway. Another option is pricing for loaners e.g. machine availability super-contracts. Zone charges have often been used to make high-cost remote location users pay their true service costs. The risk is that what is remote to one company is not to another (their machine base dispersion may be very different). Note that all these policies are made more feasible by more focused attempts to segment the market for service and by overall marketing policies designed to reinforce the image of the supplier and service.

Sensitivity to customer needs

More sensitivity to customer needs does not always cost money - it may enable response times to be lengthened (provided that all customers do not need quick response at the same time). If a loaner or reserve equipment system is operated at the discretion (and expense) of the sales point, this abolishes the need for a top-heavy prioritisation scheme. The sales point should know what it stands to win or lose by not issuing a loaner.

Customer care and customer support

Customer care programmes should only be undertaken to improve or preserve long term profit. Large customer care programmes directed from the centre are often ill-conceived, difficult to control, and uncertain in benefits. If a company has area profit responsibility, customer support would be more intelligible as a concept. Engineers can then be responsible for profit from the existing installed base. Troublesome equipment (high service cost) would be signalled as a risk by the engineer to the marketing member of his team (under general, not functional management). This also gives engineers wider roles, which may solve the excess capacity problem that exists in many companies. It requires training, and restructuring of engineer and salesforce compensation. It might involve re-assignment (e.g. engineers less capable of customer base defence jobs to service centres).

This approach might produce more effective prioritising of customer needs. The best judge of the needed level of service is the service and sales team in contact with the customer. They should know the needs for particular machines and the local competitive situation better than central negotiators. Some customers are very discriminating, but most are not. Sensible and flexible local policy, constrained by profit responsibility (which cuts both ways, via cost of quick response and cost of loss of customer), may be a better option.

APPENDIX: THIRD PARTY MAINTENANCE

This appendix analyses some aspects of third party maintenance (TPM) and the response of equipment suppliers to the challenge.

There are two main kinds of TPM, 'official' and 'pirate'. Official TPM is where equipment suppliers approve the supply of maintenance by a third party. This approval may have a contractual element, covering parts supply, area franchise, and charges. This is a common arrangement for domestic appliances, cars and smaller capital equipment (e.g. smaller business machines). The "pirate" supplier exists without approval (and sometimes with clear disapproval) of equipment suppliers, and aims to win service contracts against competition from equipment suppliers or approved maintenance suppliers.

REASONS FOR GROWTH IN TPM
Proliferation of small suppliers

Many markets (e.g. computers) are initially dominated by a few major suppliers. As the market matures, the number of suppliers increases (in computers this was reinforced by the advent of many new companies offering peripherals and microcomputer systems). Some new entrants have a widely dispersed installed base, often not economical for them to maintain. They may find it attractive to avoid complicating marketing launch problems with maintenance roll-out problems, especially if they want to negotiate wide geographic deals with major customers. These are the main factors responsible for the growth in 'official' TPM.

Increased ease of entry into the service business

Increasing ease of maintenance (reliability, modularity, etc.) means that TPM companies find it technically easier to manage a competent service operation. Technical barriers to entry have been reduced.

Profitability and higher price of service from major suppliers

The service profitability of dominant suppliers is an attractive target for TPM companies, who can sell service at a discount and still make a good profit (though not all TPM companies sell only on price). This is one reason for the growth of 'pirate' TPM. Pressure on budgets during recession increases the responsiveness of some users to TPM. One motive for using TPM is cost saving, if the customer is assured of parity in the level of service.

Slow improvement in efficiency and performance of major suppliers
The 'pirate' opportunity is increased by the slowness of some equipment suppliers to respond to the TPM threat. This response should take two forms.
1. Efficiency must be improved to reduce the premium equipment suppliers need to charge. This may be seen as hard to achieve without reducing the level of service. The service function may not tolerate this, especially if it is evaluated on level of service. Slowness to respond may be due to lack of efficiency pressure on the service function, often seen as highly profitable, when it is effectively responsible for making profit to cover most of the business. This is a greater risk for companies where service is a profit centre but without aggressive enough profit targets.
2. The level of service (in the broadest sense of the term) to customers most likely to be vulnerable to TPM must be kept up. This may not mean raising the level, but more sensitivity to variations in the level required. TPM companies are often small enough to be flexible to customer needs, with a high level of service for situations of acute need and a low level for less acute need, within the framework of a single agreement (rather than varying level of service via contract terms). Response requirements are certainly a very important reason for users choosing TPM. For some users, poor service may be a trigger for considering TPM, and cost savings the most important reason for deciding on TPM.

Range filling by TPM companies
TPM companies may take on competitive and/or complementary types of equipment, increasing installed-base density without attachment to the market share of a particular make. Some 'official' TPM companies decide to go for growth or diversification by servicing other makes on a 'pirate' basis, spreading fixed costs over more revenue, and gaining from increased installed-base density. This is more likely if there is the possibility of comprehensive service to a multivendor site. The above survey gave this as an important reason for TPM companies choosing this policy, but not for users choosing TPM. This policy can be followed by equipment suppliers, to control service prior to selling their own equipment. Using a resident engineer increases the attractiveness of this option.

Taking on microcomputer contracts is also a good option. Micros can be used more easily as fill-ins, improving engineer time utilisation, especially via take-away service at workshops or service centres.

Falling parts cost as a proportion of total cost

Parts costs may be falling as a proportion of service costs. This varies with electronic/mechanical mix, and is also impacted by fault frequency, engineer costs, machine density, and so forth. Modular replacement, central or service centre module repair, and component replacement may complicate the picture. If parts costs are falling relative to total costs, this reduces one handicap suffered by some TPM companies, who may be buying parts on unfavourable terms.

LIMITATIONS TO PIRATE PENETRATION

Various factors limit pirate TPM penetration. In particular, pirate companies may find it difficult to service new models because of:

1. Limited access to technical manuals, parts, etc. If manuals are made available by the equipment supplier as part of a distributor or user own service policy, parts pricing should if possible discriminate between distributors, own-service users and other customers. Legal issues may prevent price discrimination on a given item, so this may have to be achieved via higher general parts costs and better equipment discounts.
2. Their progress down the maintenance learning curve (generated by experience with a small proportion of the machine population) is slower.
3. The installed base density problem may be more acute with new products (with the exception of high volume products such as microcomputers).

ADVANTAGES OF EQUIPMENT SUPPLIERS AND DISTRIBUTORS

Equipment suppliers should be in a better position to service their own equipment more economically, because :
- Their installed base density should be greater (unless the supplier has a limited product range, and the "pirate" maintains a broad variety of makes), reducing travel time.
- They can attune engineer skill levels more precisely to equipment requirements, and are in a better position on test equipment. In cases where the right test equipment is not available, the TPM company may be forced to subcontract the work back to the equipment supplier, at penal

cost. This problem may be enhanced as test equipment increases in sophistication, or as remote diagnosis becomes more common.

- They have greater economies of parts inventory and a faster chain of supply from manufacture.
- They can share service costs with the marketing and administrative sides of their business, or give engineers marketing tasks.
- They are best placed to market service contracts to their customers. They know when new kit is being installed or when service contracts are due for renewal.
- Irrespective of the legal position, they may exercise influence in favour of their own service, via warranties or guarantees. Some customers prefer to have one point of liability. Sound marketing helps here.
- They are preferred suppliers for most users, since they are believed to have better equipment knowledge, service and techniques.
- They have no legal obligation to supply parts from inventory (as opposed to manufacturing). This reinforces the tendency of TPM companies to obtain spare parts from used equipment. This is a cheaper but less reliable system.
- Use of a TPM company can result in more work for the user, particularly during the change-over.
- TPM companies are prone to manpower problems (higher attrition rates, lack of promotion paths, and so forth).
- TPM suppliers often tend to pick up contracts on older equipment, which takes longer to repair and uses more obsolescent parts. This lightens the burden on official maintenance suppliers.

THE CASE OF THE COMPUTER MARKET

In the UK, the major TPM companies offer anything up to a 30% discount on original supplier prices, and claim that they deliver a better service. Manufacturers may encourage their presence when it comes to servicing a range of machines which has been or is about to be discontinued. The customer may also benefit from the effect of TPM on the supplier's own level of service and efficiency. However, some major suppliers have been pursuing an active campaign against TPM suppliers, making it difficult for them to obtain parts, diagnostic software, and the like.

Some TPM suppliers offer site discounts, attempting to capture a high proportion of the customer's service business. These discounts reflect expected economies in the use of engineers, spare parts holding, and travel time. On larger customer sites, the discounts offered by the TPM supplier may (if handled through the same budget i.e. if there is no strong distinction between capital and current budgets) allow the DP manager to use the funds to obtain incremental equipment.

Some larger TPM companies have as many engineers and customers as medium sized equipment manufacturers. The increasingly mixed-make environment of many users may favour TPM suppliers, as they offer a 'single source' for service. This tendency may grow as system interconnections become increasingly standardised. One TPM supplier, specialising in microcomputers, operates a network of service centres. The equipment may be brought in by customers, but most of it is collected by the TPM supplier for repair at the centre. Another TPM supplier specialises in mainframes. Most of its engineers are on-site.

The increasing reliability of hardware may mean that the long term market for TPM is limited. Equipment suppliers are becoming more aggressive in defence of their after-market (whether service, software or supplies), as it increases its importance as a profit contributor. TPM suppliers sometimes highlight particular deficiencies in suppliers' service policies and procedures. These may be remedied, and contracts won back. Insurance-based servicing is taking some customers back to equipment suppliers, but this time on time and materials service, not on maintenance agreements.

RELATED POLICY ISSUES IN THE SERVICE MARKET
Hardware versus aftermarket profits
Hardware markets with large after-markets (service, add-on sales, software, and supplies) may generate cross-subsidy between initial hardware sales and after-market products. As a market becomes more competitive, initial hardware discounts may increase, while after-market products are sold at an increasing premium. This is an extension of charging what the market will bear. Once the customer is caught, he has fewer sourcing options. This principle holds for many industries. In distributor markets, taking service profit on parts rather than on labour maintains the profit stream while allowing distributors to service. But with increasing parts reliability, parts are less of a key to the aftermarket, and other elements (after-sales support, supplies, and add-on sales) become more important.

Exposure to piracy

Taking profit on the aftermarket exposes suppliers to piracy, whether via TPM or competitive parts suppliers. But original suppliers who lose no business to pirates may be underpricing aftermarket products. The correct policy to follow is one which generates most profit by keeping pirating in control and allowing a good aftermarket margin. The sustainable aftermarket price premium depends on market response to the premium and relative efficiency of competing suppliers. If pirate companies are efficient, and pass this on in lower prices, the sustainable premium may not be high enough to allow equipment suppliers to achieve profit targets. The pirate is only earning profit to cover service, while the supplier may be covering machine sales with service profit. If the equipment market gets more competitive, there is corresponding pressure on suppliers to increase aftermarket margins.

Piracy and size of installed base

The risk of piracy increases the larger the installed base of a given type of equipment, as the pirate has to finance training and some parts inventory. This puts suppliers of industry-standard equipment more at risk. Piracy is less worthwhile the smaller the installed base. The risk of piracy can be reduced by design and marketing policies which encourage obsolescence (rapid product change, and associated parts change). An additional strategy is to have high usage parts specially designed or requiring special installation (e.g. within module). This may raise manufacturing costs, but the additional profit from reduced aftermarket competition can easily outweigh this.

Addiction to service contracts

Some equipment suppliers prefer contracts to per call service. They reduce the level of service on the latter to deter customers from choosing it, because it creates problems for marketing and customer administration systems that cannot handle small occasional sales (e.g. payment for one call) well. As equipment reliability increases, more customers may choose this option, which they might once have excluded because of the supposed risk of a lower level of service. The less frequent the need for service, the less the customer may be willing to pay for a service contract at all. Unless this situation is handled efficiently (e.g. via engineer billing), it can become very expensive, leading to a vicious circle of higher charges and lost business. The marketing policy here must be to allow the customer to pay as he wishes (contract or occasional payment), and ensure that the company makes a good profit either way. Otherwise, a loophole will develop for TPM companies.

Keeping hold of the service market

There are a number of ways to protect service profit, as follows:

- For parts-intensive service, ensure that parts piracy is made difficult, e.g. via parts complexity and modularity, and that official parts that end up with pirates are priced to yield the appropriate margins.
- For service which is not parts-intensive, whether due to parts repair feasibility or high relative diagnostic time (e.g. software maintenance), ensure that steps are taken to reinforce customer loyalty (contract renewal incentives, advertising, customer care actions, preventive maintenance, uptime, response time, efficiency of repair, identifying customers at risk, call prioritisation, and so on).
- Consider all ways of cutting service costs within the constraints of customer requirements, including operating practices of TPM companies.
- Ensure that service performance/profit targets are aggressive enough to yield the appropriate profit.
- Ensure that the service organisation is staffed and paid so as to reflect the need for efficiency.
- Price service so as to allow the optimal level of TPM penetration, and develop a process for continuous monitoring of this level.
- Ensure that service on a time and materials basis is available without prejudice to the customer and at a profitable price to the supplier.

Effect of installed base growth

In many markets, after-market revenue eventually outgrows revenue from new placements (the reverse of the situation during early market development). The size and accessibility of installed base-derived profits attracts TPM, often when equipment suppliers have begun to rely on that profit to discount initial placements. The larger the installed base relative to new placements, the less the after-market premium needed to aid initial placements. Medium term changes in the relative sizes of these two revenue streams need to be planned, to avoid opening up opportunities to TPM which may not be closable later.

Effect of third party distributors

The use of third party distributors is encouraged by:

- Market maturity (and its associated requirements of close contact with a variety of customers for adaptation to user needs).
- Falling price and increased maintainability (often going together due to design and manufacturing development).

These distributors usually want as much of the marketing added value as possible, including service. The solution for suppliers is rarely to resist the market pressures which lead to use of distributors, but to choose a course of long term co-operation which pays well to both parties. This may well require progressive handing over of service to distributors, with profit earned through parts, support and other after-market operations.

INDEX

Atlanta

impressions

photography and text by **Robb Helfrick**

FARCOUNTRY
PRESS

Dedication

*In memory of Greg Shorb and
dedicated to my sister Joan Shorb.
Come back to Atlanta and visit soon.*

Title page: Vibrant tulips and the bright hues of new foliage
paint an April scene in Atlanta.

Right: A footbridge and a reflective pond in Lenox Park
offer an escape from the city.

Front cover: As daylight fades, Atlanta's downtown skyline
welcomes the night with its own illumination.

Back cover: On the banks of Lake Clara Meer, native azaleas
add a colorful element to a spring setting at Piedmont Park.

ISBN 1-56037-307-5
Photography © 2004 Robb Helfrick
© 2004 Farcountry Press
Text by Robb Helfrick

For more information about our books write Farcountry Press, P.O. Box 5630,
Helena, MT 59604; call (800) 821-3874; or visit www.farcountrypress.com.

Created, produced, and designed in the United States. Printed in China.
08 07 06 05 04   1 2 3 4 5

Right: From an elevated perch on Peachtree Street, this sculpted trio is silhouetted by the morning sun.

Left: The Fountain of Rings glows during an hourly display of lights and music in Centennial Olympic Park. The fountain is the centerpiece of the park that celebrates Atlanta's hosting of the 1996 Olympic Games. It is a favorite gathering place for children, who run through the fountain's alternating sprays of cool water.

Below: The legacy of Martin Luther King Jr. is remembered in Atlanta, the home of the late civil rights leader. The King Center, which was established after his death in 1968, is a living memorial to his philosophy of nonviolent conflict resolution and social change.

Above: The lovely aroma of wisteria is often the first announcement of its presence.

Left: A quiet spot for contemplation along the west bank of the Chattahoochee River.

Below: The memory of Margaret Mitchell, writer of the legendary novel *Gone With The Wind,* is honored in Oakland Cemetery. Her tale of Atlanta during the Civil War was celebrated in the famous motion picture starring Vivian Leigh and Clark Gable. In 1949, she was struck by a speeding taxi on Peachtree Street and died from her injuries five days later.

Above: A monument on Peachtree Battle Road commemorates the fierce battle on this ground during the Civil War. In July 1864, Confederate forces disrupted the advance of Union troops on the city but were unable to prevent the capture of Atlanta in September of that year.

Facing page: In Oakland Cemetery, a monument pays tribute to loved ones at rest. The cemetery is the final home for many of Atlanta's famous and prominent past residents, as well as the common citizens of Atlanta's early years. The cemetery was created in 1850, and inside the walls of its 88 acres is a fascinating mixture of wonderful architecture, multi-cultural history, and subtle beauty.

Left: The twin spires of Sacred Heart Catholic Church rise gracefully amid modern architecture in downtown Atlanta. This French Romanesque–style church was constructed from brick and terra cotta materials and completed in 1898. The original parish church, a humble wooden structure, was located twelve blocks west of this site.

Below: Prior to the Olympic Games, donors were given the opportunity to fund a portion of Centennial Olympic Park's creation. These bricks bear the names of those generous boosters, and they represent just a few of the 800,000 bricks found in the park. If laid end to end, the bricks would stretch over 100 miles; the list of patrons is even more impressive, because they came from all over the world.

Right: The neo-Gothic facade of Atlanta City Hall absorbs the warmth of the afternoon sun.

Far right: Atlanta became Georgia's capital city in 1868, and this impressive neo-classical capitol building was completed twenty-one years later. Georgia gold leaf was utilized to adorn its dome, a fitting final touch of luster for a building that represents "the capital of the new south."

Below: The Candler Building, with its ornate architectural detail, is a monument to the late Asa Candler. A one-time mayor of Atlanta, he is better known as the founder of the Coca-Cola empire. A bottle of his famous soft drink was placed inside the building's cornerstone.

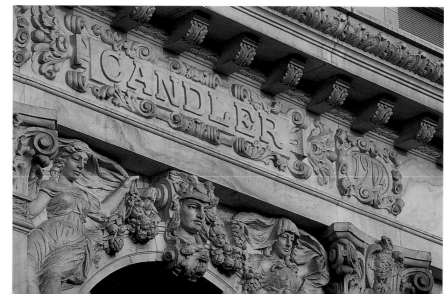

Above: This bell tower stands on the tree-lined campus of Emory University, a prestigious institution of higher learning in the charming suburb of Decatur. Founded in 1836, the University's reputation for academic excellence attracts a diverse group of international students.

Left: An aerial view of the Carter Center shows its interconnected circular architecture. The center was created by President Jimmy Carter and is home to his Presidential Library and Museum. The Carter Center also serves as an ongoing public policy organization that devotes its energy to the worldwide protection of human rights, the prevention and resolution of conflicts, and the enhancement of freedom and democracy.

Above: In Ansley Park, pear trees awaken and grass grows green during the last days of March.

Facing page: The pageantry of college football is on display during a halftime show at Georgia Tech's Bobby Dodd Stadium. Yellow Jacket fans cheer for their team, known as the "Ramblin' Wreck."

Right: At the World of Coca-Cola, the museum that celebrates the history of the soft drink, red is a popular color.

Far right: A blazing summer sun slowly sinks behind the Atlanta skyline, as seen from the summit of Stone Mountain.

Left: The moon rises over the Bank of America Plaza in midtown Atlanta. A stepped pyramid with an open steel frame tops the 1,023-foot structure, which is the tallest building in the South. Just 23 feet shorter than the famed Chrysler Building in New York, it is currently the world's nineteenth tallest building.

Far left: A mammoth Argentinosaurus, thought to be the largest dinosaur ever discovered, dominates the atrium at the Fernbank Museum of Natural History. The museum opened in 1992 and is surrounded by Fernbank Forest, one of America's largest urban woodlands.

Right: Seen from the shore of Lake Allatoona, the morning sun burns through an October mist. A popular place for fishing and boating, the lake was created by the impoundment of the clear-running Etowah River.

Below: Another active day takes off at Atlanta's Hartsfield-Jackson International Airport. Known for its efficiency, it is host to over 2,400 flights a day and is the busiest passenger airport in the world.

Above: The Chattahoochee Nature Center, located on the river's bank in Roswell, rehabilitates and releases injured birds of prey. When a treated bird is unable to survive on its own in the wild, like the red-tailed hawk pictured here, it becomes a resident of the center and helps educate visitors about the importance of wildlife protection.

Left: In the shallows of the Chattahoochee River, a fisherman casts into the cool, reflective waters in search of his catch. A series of parks stretch along the river's meandering path, offering Atlantans recreation with a hint of wilderness inside the city limits.

Right: A couple shares a dockside view of a Lake Allatoona sunset. The lake, with its 270 miles of shoreline, is a recreation magnet that draws visitors from all over the Atlanta area. Along with its northern neighbor Lake Lanier, it is a prime destination for a weekend getaway of water skiing, hiking, or just plain relaxing.

Below: The torchlike shapes of Hermes Towers, decorative elements found in Centennial Olympic Park, are silhouetted by the setting sun.

Left: A fountain and a colorful array of lights beckon nighttime visitors to Kenny's Alley, a popular entertainment venue at Underground Atlanta. The area known as Underground was created when portions of the downtown area were raised one street level during the 1920s. The concrete viaducts overhead concealed the storefronts below, which have been restored and transformed into a popular area of shops, restaurants, and nightclubs.

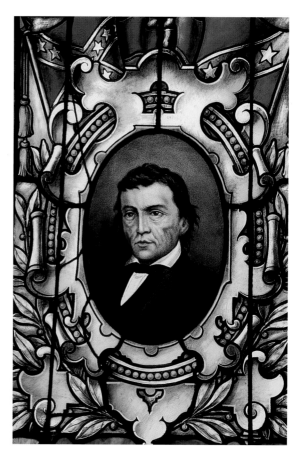

Above and left: The story of the Confederacy is told in stained glass at Rhodes Hall, former home of furniture magnate Amos Rhodes. The window at left depicts Joe Johnston, the Confederate general who commanded the South's futile attempt to protect Atlanta. The above image is a likeness of Alexander Stephens, Georgia's native son and Vice President of the Confederacy.

Right: Orchids abound at the Fuqua Orchid Center in the Atlanta Botanical Garden. The center houses a vast array of these delicate plants, many of which are indigenous to South America.

Below: On the rocky summit of Kennesaw Mountain, a close-up view highlights a trio of natural elements.

Left: A hint of the fall season is found on the grounds of the Atlanta Botanical Garden.

Far left: Autumn colors soften the view from a streamside path at Sweetwater Creek State Park. Upstream from this sight are the ruins of the New Manchester Manufacturing Company, a textile mill destroyed during the Civil War.

Facing page: The "Gateway of Dreams" pays tribute to Baron Pierre de Coubertin, the founder of the modern Olympic Games. The sculpture is part of Olympic history in Centennial Olympic Park.

Right and below: An orangutan and a pair of lions are among the many exotic residents of Zoo Atlanta.

35

Left: Union re-enactors wait for the battle to commence on a foggy morning at Kennesaw Mountain National Battlefield Park.

Below: A young Georgia pine is encased in ice—the result of one of Atlanta's occasional winter storms.

Right: A neon Coke bottle shares the night sky with the Georgia state capitol dome in downtown.

Facing page: The Westin Peachtree Plaza rises 723 feet above downtown Atlanta. The 73-story structure was the tallest hotel in the world when it premiered in 1976. The revolving restaurant and public observatory at its top offer a magnificent view of the city.

Above: "The Big Chicken" is the affectionate nickname of this Marietta landmark. For years, it has served as a roadside reference point in suburban Cobb County.

Left: In 1996, the world's premier athletes came to Atlanta to compete in the Summer Olympic Games. In this scene at Olympic Stadium, 200-meter contestants round the turn and head for the tape.

41

Right: An evening reflection on smooth running water is interrupted by a shoal as the Chattahoochee River flows south toward Paces Ferry.

Below: Martin Luther King Jr. grew up on Atlanta's Auburn Avenue. He rose to prominence as the leader of America's Civil Rights Movement and was awarded the 1964 Nobel Peace Prize. His life tragically was cut short in 1968, but his spirit carries on through the noble work of the King Center. He rests on his beloved "Sweet Auburn" Avenue, just a short distance from his boyhood home.

Left: A lovely modern-day Scarlett O'Hara in Jonesboro, home of the mythical "Tara" plantation made famous in *Gone With The Wind*.

Far left: The Battle of Atlanta is depicted on the world's largest painting, 358 feet in circumference, found at the Atlanta Cyclorama. This small section of the work shows the fine detail of the creation as well as the accompanying three-dimensional figures (at the bottom of the photograph) that add depth to the 40-foot-tall artwork. The painting is viewed from the center of a large circular room and is a must-see for anyone interested in Civil War history.

Above: The Atlanta Steeplechase is one of the most anticipated social events of the spring season. Held annually on a Saturday in April, this traditional countryside event is the site of spirited racing competition—as well as a place for ladies to show off their fashionable headwear.

Facing page: The High Museum of Art is a contemporary treasure that boasts an impressive collection of European, African, and American folk art.

Left: Former Brave and Hall of Fame player Warren Spahn is remembered outside Turner Field as the greatest left-handed pitcher in major-league history. His 363 wins are the most ever for a southpaw.

Far left: A Sunday afternoon Braves game at Turner Field is a popular Atlanta pastime.

Below: Hank Aaron is a baseball legend and his classic swing is immortalized at Turner Field. Aaron set many records during his twenty-three-year career, the most memorable being his seven hundred fifteenth home run, which surpassed Babe Ruth's record for most home runs in baseball history. He would go on to smash seven hundred fifty-five home runs and earn the respect as one of the best to ever play the game. Aaron was inducted into the Hall of Fame, and today he is an active member of the Braves organization and the Atlanta community.

Above: A church window in historic Marietta exudes a warm holiday glow.

Right: With its striking skyline, Atlanta's midtown is known for its modern architecture. The area is home to cultural attractions such as the Woodruff Art Center, High Museum of Art, and Atlanta Botanical Garden. Midtown is also home to lovely neighborhoods and Atlanta's outdoor gathering place, Piedmont Park.

Stone Mountain is a geologic wonder. The largest body of exposed granite in the world, it towers 825 feet above the neighboring countryside. In 1972, a massive carving of Confederate heroes—Stonewall Jackson (shown at left), Jefferson Davis, and Robert E. Lee (shown below)—was completed on the mountain. It is the largest high-relief sculpture in the world. The area surrounding the mountain is home to a park administered by the state of Georgia.

Right: A pond mirrors one of the circular buildings found on the grounds of the Carter Center. The center is a destination for visitors with an interest in presidential history as well as those who enjoy the peaceful allure of its natural surroundings.

Below: This grist mill, on the grounds of Stone Mountain Park, is a relic of bygone days.

Above: Azaleas on West Paces Ferry Road announce the arrival of spring.

Left: Atlanta's pleasant climate provides ideal growing conditions for a variety of plant life.

Facing page: The Georgia Institute of Technology has achieved a well-deserved reputation as a top engineering and research center. The university's students co-mingle in midtown Atlanta with big business and a vibrant art community.

Below: This trolley barn in Inman Park serves as a link to the past.

Left: This playful public sculpture in Centennial Olympic Park pays tribute to the gathering of athletes who came in the spirit of competition from points all over the globe.

Below: Atlanta's Fourth of July celebration would not be complete without the annual running of the Peachtree Road Race. The world's largest 10K road race (last count: 55,000 participants) began in 1970 with only 110 runners. The challenging course winds it way down Peachtree Street, and the simple reward for many who run is the coveted Peachtree Road Race T-shirt, which sports a different design each year.

Right: Southern soldiers are laid to rest in curving rows in Marietta's Confederate Cemetery. There are 3,000 departed Civil War veterans interred here, a somber testament to the most devastating war in American history.

Below: On a lakeside pathway in Piedmont Park, lilies await those who stroll in Atlanta's favorite gathering place. The park was designed in part by famous landscape architect Frederick Law Olmstead and it recently celebrated its one hundredth birthday.

Above: Dogwoods flower in March and April in parks and neighborhoods all over the city.

Left: An aerial view of Atlanta shows the downtown skyline, CNN Center, Centennial Olympic Park, and the Georgia Dome. The Dome is home to the Atlanta Falcons, the city's NFL representative, and has hosted a number of high-profile sporting events such as the Super Bowl and NCAA Final Four.

Right: A Japanese garden filled with the multi-colored hues of azaleas is a treat for those who venture outside the Carter Presidential Museum and Library.

Below: A statue honoring businessman and art patron Robert Woodruff graces the grounds of the Woodruff Arts Center in midtown. The Atlanta Symphony makes beautiful music here.

Above: Robert E. Lee and his horse Traveler are immortalized in stained glass at historic Rhodes Hall.

Left: A winter sky burns bright at dusk on the summit of Little Kennesaw Mountain.

On Auburn Avenue, Atlanta's cultural center for its African-American community,
colorful outdoor artwork adorns a building near the King Center.

A coneflower in a Georgia garden.

A red tulip soaks up the rain in Sandy Springs.

THE DOROTHY CHAPMAN FUQUA CONSERVATORY

Left: In Woodruff Park a sculpture remembers Atlanta's rise from almost total destruction during the Civil War into what is now a beautiful modern city.

Far left: The Fuqua Conservatory is bathed in morning light on the grounds of the Atlanta Botanical Garden. It is the centerpiece of a lovely garden complex that was built on a gentle hill overlooking Piedmont Park.

Right: The Georgia state capitol lights up the night sky in downtown Atlanta.

Facing page: The supreme effort of those who chase Olympic glory shows on the faces of the figures found on "The Last Meter," a captivating work of art in Piedmont Park.

Left: The atrium of the CNN Center was once the home of an indoor theme park but is now a bustling center of activity at the headquarters of the world's best-known cable network. From this location, CNN broadcasts news events to over one billion people worldwide and also offers public studio tours that provide a behind-the-scenes glimpse of the fast-paced news industry.

Far left: At the entrance to one of the finest entertainment venues in the South, there is no doubt what city is home to Philips Arena.

Above: Jimmy Carter's accomplishments as commander in chief are highlighted on the Wall of Presidents at the Carter Presidential Library

Left: This nostalgic scene in suburban Marietta is a reminder that Atlanta began as a railroad town originally called "Terminus." The end of the Western and Atlantic Railroad was the point of origin for the new city, which was later incorporated as "Marthasville" in 1842. The name was changed in honor of former Governor Lumpkin's daughter Martha, whose middle name happened to be "Atalanta," which was changed slightly to the current moniker in 1845.

*R*obb Helfrick lives in Atlanta and specializes in location photography for editorial and corporate clients. His photographs have appeared in many national publications, including *National Geographic Traveler, Sierra, Hemispheres, Travel Holiday, Sky, National Geographic Adventure,* and *Audubon.* Close to home, he is a regular contributor to *Atlanta* and *Georgia* magazines. Robb was the sole photographer for both *The Civil War in Georgia* and the Fodor travel guide *Georgia.* His work was featured exclusively in the Farcountry Press books *Savannah Impressions, North Carolina Simply Beautiful* and *St. Augustine Impressions.* His photographs were also featured with noted landscape photographer James Randklev in the Farcountry book *Georgia Simply Beautiful.* Robb is a recipient of the Len Foote Memorial Award for Conservation Photography and he has won numerous other awards for his work.

Robb's images are sold and exhibited through his Atlanta-based photographic agency. In addition to his location assignments around the United States, he is currently photographing the South's foremost travel cities for a new book.